6B

Maths — No Problem!

Singapore Maths
English National Curriculum 2014

Consultant
Dr. Yeap Ban Har

UK Consultant
Dr. Anne Hermanson

Author
Brandon Oh

Published by Maths — No Problem!
Copyright © 2018 by Maths — No Problem!

Printed in the United Kingdom
First Printing, 2016
Reprinted once in 2016, twice in 2017 and in 2018

ISBN 978-1-910504-23-9

Maths — No Problem!
Dowding House, Coach & Horses Passage
Tunbridge Wells, UK TN2 5NP

www.mathsnoproblem.com

Acknowledgements

This Maths — No Problem! series, adapted from the New Syllabus
Primary Mathematics series, is published in collaboration with
Shing Lee Publishers. Pte Ltd. The publisher would like to thank
Dr. Tony Gardiner for his contribution.

Design and Illustration by Kin

Preface

Maths — No Problem! is a comprehensive series that adopts a spiral design with carefully built-up mathematical concepts and processes adapted from the maths mastery approaches used in Singapore. The Concrete-Pictorial-Abstract (C-P-A) approach forms an integral part of the learning process through the materials developed for this series.

Maths — No Problem! incorporates the use of concrete aids and manipulatives, problem-solving and group work.

In Maths — No Problem! Primary 6, these features are exemplified throughout the chapters:

Worksheet

Well-structured exercises which are developed in accordance with the lesson objectives of each chapter.

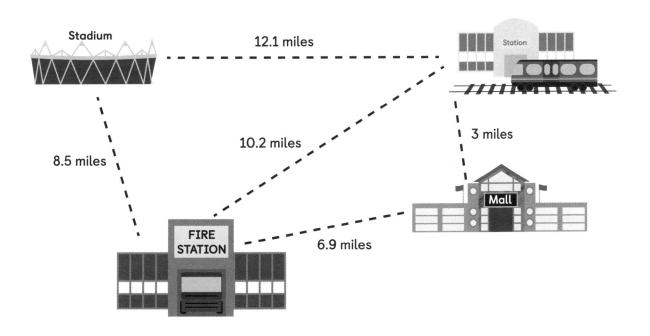

Mind Workout

Higher-order thinking tasks as enrichment for pupils to apply relevant heuristics and extend the concepts and skills learnt.

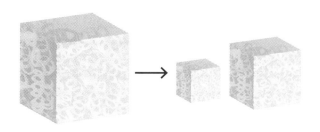

Review

Follows after each chapter for consolidation of concepts learnt in the chapter.

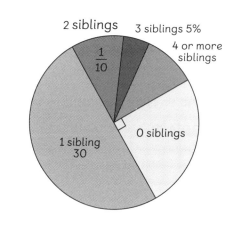

Revision

Provides an assessment of the consolidation of concepts and skills across strands and topics.

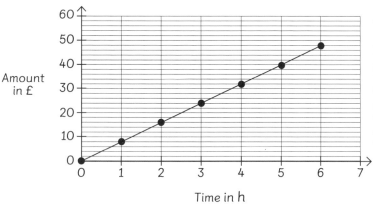

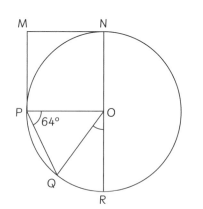

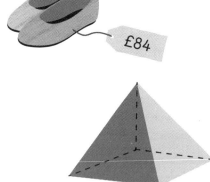

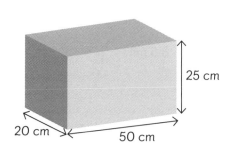

Contents

Chapter 10 Area and Perimeter

Chapter 11 Volume

Chapter 12   Geometry

Chapter 13   Position and Movement

Chapter 14

Graphs and Averages

Chapter 15

Negative Numbers

Percentage

Chapter 7

Name: _____ Class: _____ Date: _28/1/80_

Worksheet 1

Finding a Percentage of a Number

Find the value of each of the following.

1 30% of 120

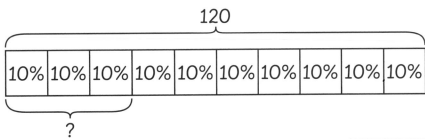

36

2 60% of 300

180

3 70% of 65

s̶6̶5̶0
19.5
45.5

45.5

4 The table shows the percentage of each type of cookie a baker made.

Type of cookies	Percentage
Chocolate Chip	35%
Oatmeal Raisin	10%
Almond	55%

She made a total of 500 cookies.

(a) How many oatmeal raisin cookies did she make?

50

(b) How many chocolate chip cookies did she make?

175

(c) How many almond cookies did she make?

275

Name: _____ Class: _____ Date: 28/4/20

Finding a Percentage of a Quantity

1 Lulu made some orange squash by mixing 2 l of water with 500 ml of orange cordial.

(a) Out of 100, how many parts of the mixture is orange cordial?

100 parts

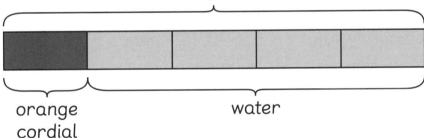

orange   water
cordial

5 units = | 100 | parts

1 unit = | 20 | ÷ 5

     = | 20 | out of 100 parts of the mixture is orange cordial.

There is | 20 | ml of orange cordial in every 100 ml of the drink.

| 20 | % of the mixture is orange cordial.

(b)   Lulu wants to make 4 l of the squash drink. How many ml of orange cordial will she need?

1000

2   [   ] represents Mr Smith's monthly salary.

Answer these questions.

(a)   Mr Smith spends 40% of his monthly salary on rent. Shade to show 40% of his salary.

(b)   Mr Smith's monthly salary is £3600. He spends 25% of his monthly salary on food. How much does he spend on food?

£3600

£900

3 Calculate the prices of these items after the discount.

(a)

£75

40% discount

$$\begin{array}{r} 2\overset{}{7}.5 \\ \times\ 4 \\ \hline 3\ 0\ 0 \end{array}$$

£45

(b)

£350

5% discount

$$\begin{array}{r} 3\overset{4}{\cancel{8}}\overset{\overset{9}{\cancel{8}}}{\cancel{8}}\overset{1}{0} \\ 1\ 7.5 \\ \hline 3\ 3\ 2\ 5 \end{array}$$

£332.50

(c)

£500

5%
discount

£475

4 Elliott spent 20% of his savings on toys and 50% of the rest on food. He then had £80 left. How much did Elliott have in savings to begin with?

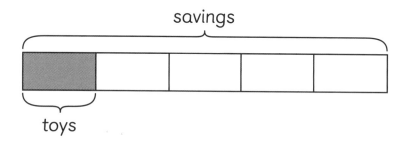

savings

toys

£80 = 30%

$\begin{array}{r} 26.66 \\ \overline{3|8^2 0} \end{array}$

£266.80

5 Lulu painted 20% of a fence white and 25% of the rest blue. The part of the fence painted blue was 60 m long. What is the total length of the fence?

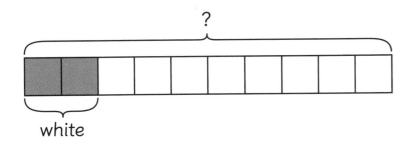

?

white

300 m

6 A baker used 40% of a bag of flour to bake cakes and 50% of the remaining flour to bake biscuits. At the end, he had 69 kg of flour left. What was the initial weight of the bag of flour?

230 kg

Name: _____ Class: _____ Date: 14/3/20

Worksheet 3

Finding Percentage Change

1 Miss Meharg wants to increase the price of the food in her café by 20%. Find the new prices of these items.

(a)

fries £2

2.40

(b)

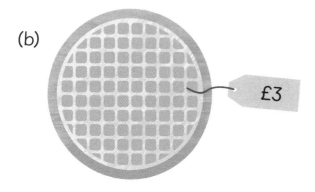

£3

£3.60

(c)

£6

£7.20

2 The price of a concert ticket has increased by 10%. The new price is £220. What was the price of the ticket before the increase?

£200

3 The price of a watch has increased by 50%. What was the original price of the watch?

£300

Worksheet 4

Using Percentage to Compare

Class	Number of pupils
A	28
B	35
C	42

(a)   Class B has [25] % more pupils than Class A.

(b)   Class C has [20] % more pupils than Class B.

(c)   Class C has [50] % more pupils than Class A.

2 The grey bowl contains 120 jelly beans and the white bowl contains 96 jelly beans.

The white bowl contains [20] % fewer jelly beans than the grey bowl.

3   and his friends went fruit picking in an orchard.

 I picked 50 raspberries.

 I picked 30% more raspberries than .

 I picked 30% fewer raspberries than .

(a) How many raspberries did pick?

65

(b) How many raspberries did pick?

35

Mind Workout

Date: 19/3/20

The total number of pears and oranges in a basket is between 30 and 40. There are 25% more pears than oranges. How many pears are there in the basket?

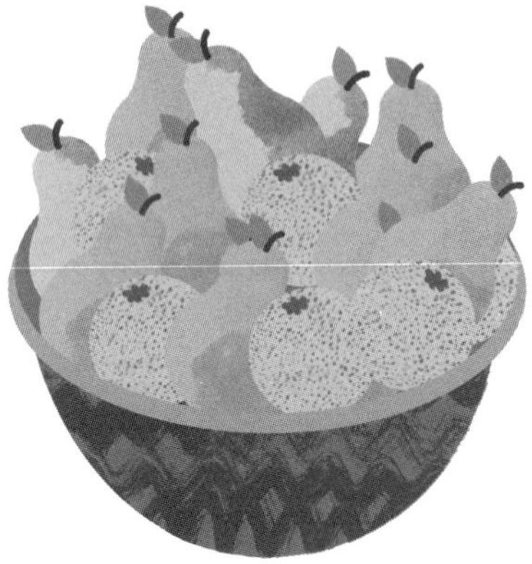

20 pears

Name: _____ **Class:** _____ **Date:** 19/3/20

Review 7

1 We represent the number of animals in a pet shop by the rectangle:

(a) 30% of the animals in the pet shop are dogs. Shade to show 30%.

(b) 60% of the animals in the pet shop are rabbits. Shade to show 60%.

2

 is 40 % taller than .

 is [ ] % shorter than .

3 At a concert, 60% of the audience are adults. 25% of those remaining are boys and the rest of the audience members are girls. There are 30 girls altogether. How many people are there at the concert?

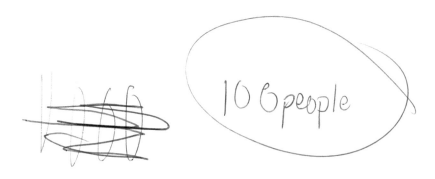

100 people

4 A dress cost £250. The dress was discounted 30% in a sale. How much did the dress cost after the discount?

£205

5 A school expected 300 people to turn up for the school musical, but 15% more than the expected number turned up. How many people turned up for the musical?

345

6 26 eggs in a carton were broken. This was 5% of the total number of eggs in the carton. How many eggs were in the carton altogether?

320

School	Number of pupils
Ethon School	700
Richmond School	200

(a) 35% of the pupils from Ethon School walk to school. How many pupils from Ethon School walk to school?

245

(b) 50% of the pupils from Richmond School wear spectacles. How many Richmond School pupils wear spectacles?

100

(c) Hillview School has 40 more students than Richmond School. When comparing the two schools, how many more pupils does Hillview have as a percentage?

20%

Ratio

LISJJ

Chapter 8

Name: _____ Class: _____ Date: 24/2/20

Worksheet 1

Comparing Quantities

1 Fill in the blanks.

(a)

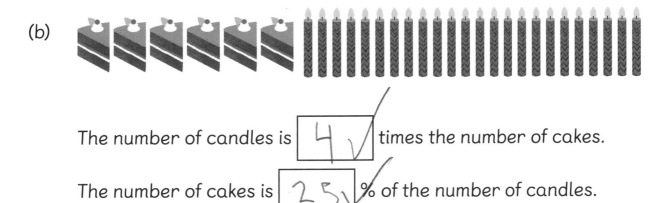

The number of apples is [5 ✓] times the number of oranges.

The number of oranges is [1/5 ✓] the number of apples.

For every 1 orange, there are [5 ✓] apples.

(b)

The number of candles is [4 ✓] times the number of cakes.

The number of cakes is [25 ✓] % of the number of candles.

For every [1 ✓] cake, there are [4 ✓] candles.

(c)

The number of girls is [2 ✓] times the number of boys.

The number of boys is [1/3 ✓] the number of children.

For every 1 boy, there are [2 ✓] girls.

For every [4 ✓] girls, there are 2 boys.

(d)

The number of buttons is [3 ✓] times the number of cotton reels.

The number of cotton reels is [1/3 ✓] the number of buttons.

For every [3 ✓] buttons, there is 1 cotton reel.

For every 12 buttons, there are [4 ✓] cotton reels.

LL

Worksheet 2

Comparing Quantities

1 Fill in the blanks.

(a)

For every 4 pens, there are | 10 ✓ | pencils.

For every 2 pens, there are | 5 ✓ | pencils.

(b)

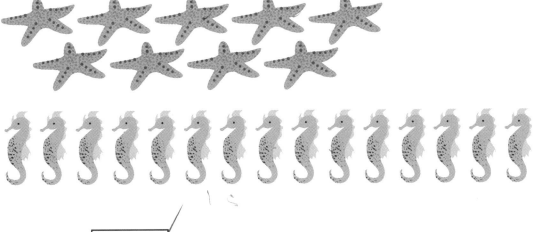

For every | 15 ✓ | seahorses, there are 9 starfish.

For every 5 seahorses, there are | 3 ✓ | starfish.

(c)

For every [16 ✓] squares, there are 12 triangles.

For every [~~4~~ 6] triangles, there are 8 squares.

For every 3 triangles, there are [4] squares. ✓

(d)

27

18

For every [27 ✓] grey circles, there are 18 white circles.

For every [9 ✓] grey circles, there are 6 white circles.

For every 3 grey circles, there are [2 ✓] white circles.

LI

✓✓

Worksheet 3

Comparing Quantities

1 Fill in the blanks.

Cake Recipe

Ingredients:
3 eggs   3 cups flour
1 cup milk $\frac{1}{2}$ cup cocoa powder
1 cup oil
2 cups sugar   1 tablespoon bicarbonate of soda

(a) For every cup of oil, we need   2   cups of sugar.

The ratio of the number of cups of oil to the number of cups of

sugar is   1 : 2 . ✓

(b) For every   3   cups of flour, we need 1 cup of milk.

The ratio of the number of cups of flour to the number of cups of

milk is   3 : 1 . ✓

(c) For every   3   cups of flour, we need   2   cups of sugar.

The ratio of the number of cups of flour to the number of cups of

sugar is   3 : 2 . ✓

2 Ruby wants to make a strawberry milkshake. Some of the ingredients she needs are shown.

2 cups of chilled milk   20 strawberries   2 cups of vanilla ice cream

(a)   For every cup of chilled milk, she needs | 10 | strawberries.

The ratio of the number of cups of chilled milk to the number of

strawberries is | 1 | : | 10 | . ✓

(b)   For every cup of vanilla ice cream, she needs | 1 | cup of chilled

milk.

The ratio of the number of cups of vanilla ice cream to the number of

cups of chilled milk is | 1 | : | 1 | . ✓

(c)   For every | 10 | strawberries, she needs 1 cup of vanilla ice cream.

The ratio of the number of strawberries to the number of cups of

vanilla ice cream is | 10 | : | 1 | . ✓

LI ✓ //

Worksheet 4

Comparing Quantities

1 Fill in the blanks.

(a)

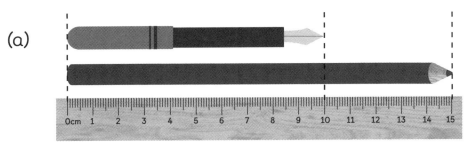

The length of the pen is $\dfrac{2}{3}$ the length of the pencil.

The ratio of the length of the pen to the length of the pencil is

| 2 | : | 3 | . ✓

(b)

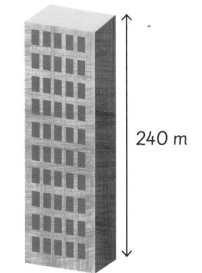

240 m

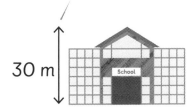

30 m

The height of the building is [8] times the height of the school.

The ratio of the height of the building to the height of the school is

| 8 | : | 8 | .

2 A rope is cut into two parts so that the ratio of the length of the shorter piece to that of the longer piece is 3 : 4.

(a) If the original length of the rope is 14 cm, what is the length of the shorter piece?

6 cm ✓

(b) If the length of the longer piece is 36 cm, what is the length of the shorter piece?

27 cm ✓

(c) If the length of the shorter piece is 24 cm, what is the original length of the rope?

56 cm ✓

Name: _____ **Class:** _____ **Date:** _14/3/20_

Worksheet 5

Comparing Quantities

1 Fill in the blanks.

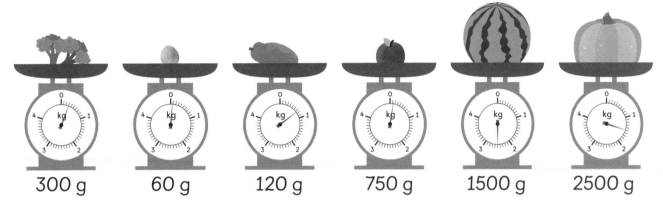

| 300 g | 60 g | 120 g | 750 g | 1500 g | 2500 g |

(a)   Find the ratio of the mass of the apple to that of the egg.

2 : 25

(b)   Find the ratio of the mass of the egg to that of the broccoli.

1 : 5

(c)   Find the ratio of the mass of the pumpkin to that of the watermelon.

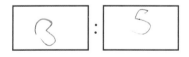
3 : 5

(d)   Find the ratio of the mass of the papaya to that of the pumpkin.

 :

(e)   Which two items have masses that are in the ratio 2 : 5?

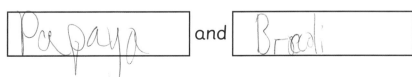
Papaya   and   Brocoli

2 Last year, the ratio of Amira's mass to that of her sister was 5 : 3. This year, the ratio is 4 : 3.

(a)   Who is heavier, Amira or her sister?

Amira

(b)   If Amira was 35 kg last year, how heavy was her sister?

21 kg

(c)   This year, Amira's sister's mass is 6 kg more than it was last year.
Is Amira's mass this year more or less than it was last year?
What is the difference?

3 kg

Worksheet 6

Comparing Numbers

1 Write each ratio in its simplest form.

(a)   3 : 9   = [1] : [3]

(b)   12 : 15   = [4] : [5]

(c)   20 : 18   = [10] : [9]

(d)   80 : 120 = [2] : [3]

(e)   75 : 255 = [5] : [17]

(f)   144 : 81 = [48] : [27]   48 : 27

2 In each of the following groups, circle the ratio that is different from the others.

(a)   10 : 6   (12 : 8)   15 : 9   20 : 12

(b)   6 : 9   12 : 18   20 : 30   (15 : 25)

(c)   14 : 6   28 : 12   (10 : 4)   7 : 3

(d)   (25 : 30)   28 : 35   12 : 15   32 : 40

3 The ratio of one number to another is 2 : 7. The sum of the two numbers is 72. What are the numbers?

16 ↑ 56

4 The ratio of one number to another is 8 : 5. The difference between the two numbers is 18. Find the two numbers.

8 : 5
48 : 30

5 The ratio of one number to another is 5 : 6. One of the numbers is 30. What are the possible values of the other number?

36/25

Worksheet 7

Solving Word Problems

1 Sam had £468. He spent some of it and saved the rest. The ratio of the amount he spent to the amount he saved is 5 : 1. How much did Sam spend?

saved

spent

£468
078
x 5
£396

2 A jar contains 840 ml of water. All the water in the jar is poured into two glasses so that the ratio of the volume of water in the first glass to that in the second glass is 2 : 5. How much water is there in each glass?

first glass

second glass

840 ml

G1 = 240

G2 = 600

3 The ratio of the mass of an empty pot to the mass of the same pot filled with soil is 2 : 11. The mass of the soil in the pot is 630 g. What is the mass of the pot?

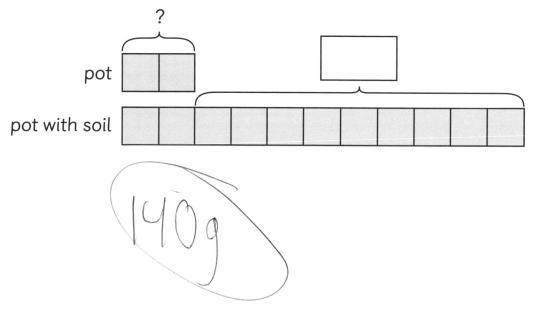

140g

4 The ratio of Holly's age to that of her aunt is 4 : 9. When Holly was born, her aunt was 15 years old. How old is Holly's aunt now?

27

Worksheet 8

Solving Word Problems

1 In a school, the ratio of the number of boys to the number of girls is 3 : 2. The ratio of the number of boys to the number of teachers is 9 : 1. There are 300 pupils altogether. How many teachers are there in the school?

boys

girls

teachers

?

20

2 At a funfair, the ratio of the number of boys to the number of girls is 4 : 3. The ratio of the number of adults to the number of girls is 3 : 2. There are 342 adults. How many boys are there at the funfair?

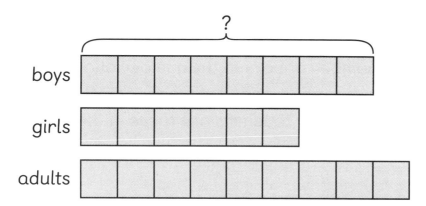

3 There are three types of sweets in a jar, 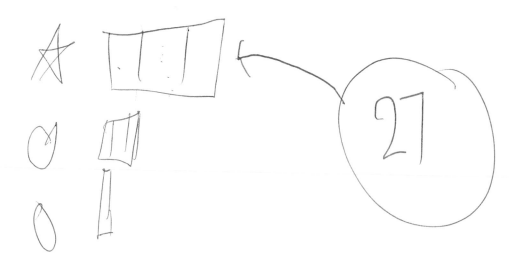. The ratio of the number of ⭐ to the number of ♥ is 3 : 1. The ratio of the number of ♥ to the number of ● is also 3 : 1. There are 39 sweets in the jar. Find the number of ⭐ in the jar.

4 Hannah baked some chocolate chip cookies, some butter cookies and some raisin cookies. The ratio of the number of chocolate chip cookies to the number of butter cookies she baked is 2 : 3. She baked 24 more raisin cookies than chocolate chip cookies. Hannah baked 143 cookies in all. How many raisin cookies did she bake?

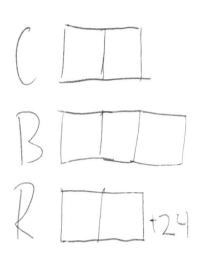

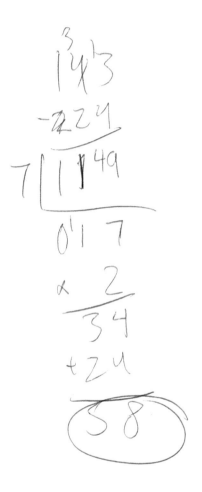

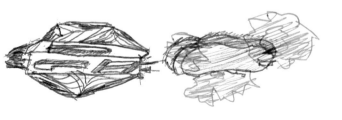

Worksheet 9

Solving Word Problems

1. The ratio of the number of apples to the number of oranges at a fruit stall is 8 : 3. After 28 oranges and 98 apples are sold, there are equal numbers of apples and oranges. How many apples and oranges were there to begin with?

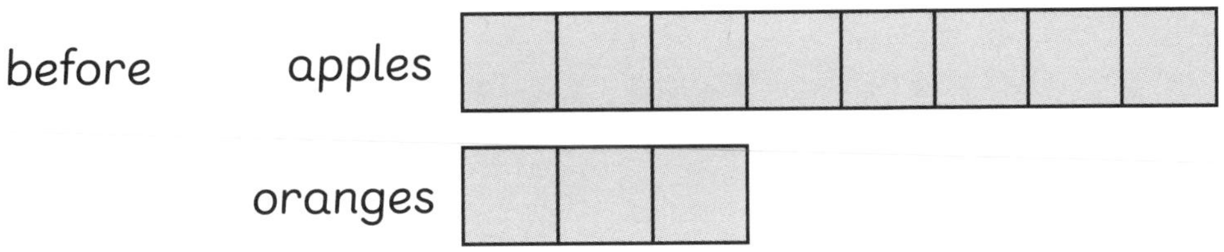

before   apples

oranges

2 In an equipment room, the ratio of the number of basketballs to the number of footballs is 4 : 5. When 72 footballs are taken out of the room, twice as many basketballs as footballs are left. Find the number of basketballs.

basketballs

footballs

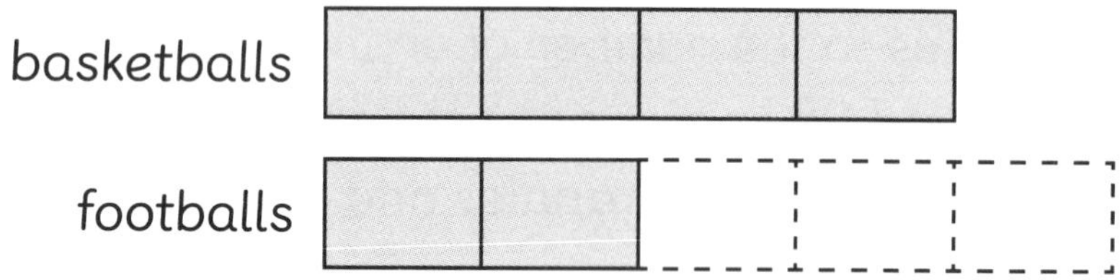

3 The ratio of the volume of water in Container A to that in Container B is 2 : 1. When 482 ml of water is poured from Container A into Container B, the ratio becomes 3 : 2. How much water is there in both the containers in total?

4 When Charles was born, his father was 25 years old. Five years ago, the ratio of Charles' age to that of his father was 3 : 8. How old is Charles' father now?

Date:_____

In a shop, a lemon pie costs £3 while a cherry pie costs £7. The ratio of the number of lemon pies to the number of cherry pies sold in a day was 3 : 7. A total of £1160 was collected from the sale of both kinds of pie. How many lemon pies and how many cherry pies were sold?

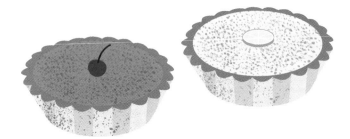

Review 8

1 Write each ratio in its simplest form.

(a) 5 : 25 = [   ] : [   ]

(b) 24 : 18 = [   ] : [   ]

(c) 56 : 72 = [   ] : [   ]

(d) 125 : 100 = [   ] : [   ]

(e) 123 : 369 = [   ] : [   ]

(f) 310 : 186 = [   ] : [   ]

2 A plank of wood is cut into two parts such that the ratio of the length of the shorter part to that of the longer part is 4 : 5.

(a) If the original length of the plank of wood is 81 cm, what is the length of the longer part?

[   ]

(b) If the length of the longer part is 100 cm, what is the length of the shorter part?

[   ]

(c) If the length of the shorter part is 84 cm, what is the original length of the plank of wood?

[   ]

3 In a section of a library, there are cookbooks, mystery books and puzzle books. The ratio of the number of cookbooks to the number of mystery books is 5 : 2. The ratio of the number of puzzle books to the number of cookbooks is 4 : 3. There are 120 puzzle books. Find the total number of books.

4 Emma buys a pack of stickers that contains furry stickers, shiny stickers and glow-in-the-dark stickers. The ratio of the number of furry stickers to the number of shiny stickers is 3 : 5. There are 32 fewer glow-in-the-dark stickers than furry stickers. There are 221 stickers altogether. Find the number of glow-in-the-dark stickers in the pack.

5 The ratio of the number of boys to the number of girls in a hall is 6 : 5. When 20 girls leave the hall and 20 boys enter the hall, the ratio becomes 2 : 1. How many children were there in the hall at first?

Algebra

Chapter 9

Name: _____ Class: _____ Date: 3/2/20

Worksheet 1

Describing a Pattern

1 arranged some marbles according to a rule.

Pattern 1 Pattern 2 Pattern 3 Pattern 4

(a)   Complete the table.

Pattern number	Number of marbles
1	1
2	2
4	4
10	10
x	x

(b)   Draw Pattern 6 and Pattern 8.

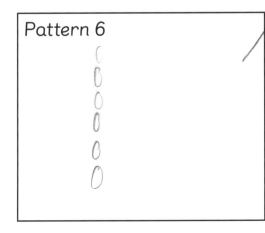

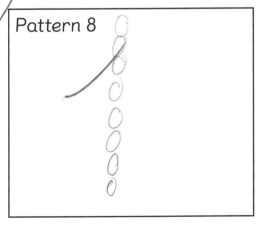

2 made this pattern using building blocks.

 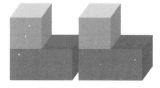 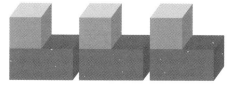

Pattern 1   Pattern 2   Pattern 3

(a)   Complete the table.

Pattern number	Number of cubes	Number of cuboids
1	1	1
2	2	2
3	3	3
7	7	7
12	12	12
y	y	y

(b)   Draw Pattern 5.

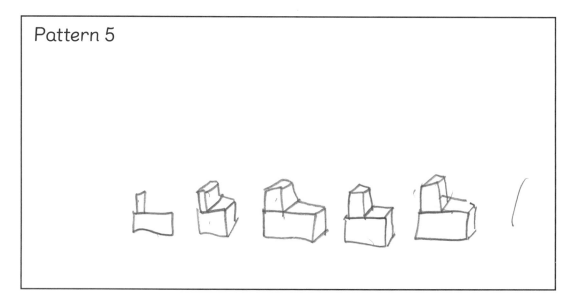

Pattern 5

How many cubes and cuboids are there altogether in Pattern 5?

10

Name: _____ Class: _____ Date: 3/2/20

Worksheet 2

Describing a Pattern

1 drew squares and triangles to make a pattern according to a rule.

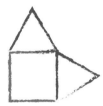 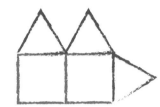 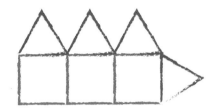

Pattern 1   Pattern 2   Pattern 3

(a) Complete the table.

Pattern number	Number of squares	Number of triangles
1	1	2
2	2	3
3	3	4
4	4	5
8	8	9
11	11	12

(b) Describe Pattern *n*.

Pattern number	Number of squares	Number of triangles
n	n × 1	2 + n + 1

2 Write down the consecutive whole numbers starting with *a*.

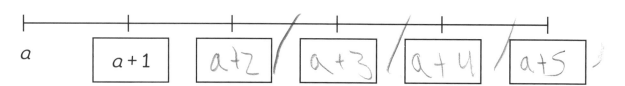

a | *a* + 1 | a+2 | a+3 | a+4 | a+5

3 Write down the consecutive even numbers starting with *b*.

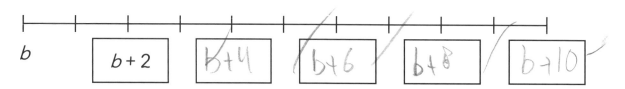

b | *b* + 2 | b+4 | b+6 | b+8 | b+10

4 Write down the consecutive odd numbers starting with *c*.

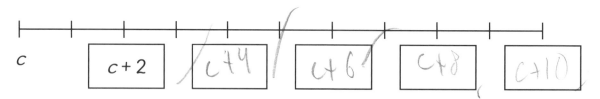

c | *c* + 2 | c+4 | c+6 | c+8 | c+10

5 What is the fifth consecutive whole number starting with *d*?

d+4

6 What is the seventh consecutive even number starting with *e*?

e+12

7 The fifth term in a sequence of consecutive whole numbers is n. What is the first term?

n−4

Worksheet 3

Describing a Pattern

1 Fill in the missing consecutive whole numbers in terms of p.

(a)

p $p+1$ $p+2$ $p+3$ $p+4$

(b)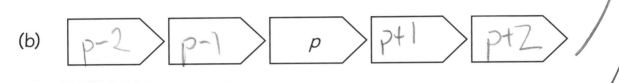

$p-2$ $p-1$ p $p+1$ $p+2$

(c)

$p-4$ $p-3$ $p+2$ $p-1$ p

2 Fill in the missing consecutive odd numbers in terms of q.

(a)

q $q+2$ $q+4$ $q+6$ $q+8$

(b)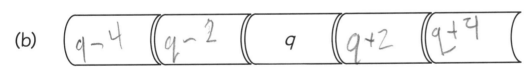

$q-4$ $q-2$ q $q+2$ $q+4$

(c)

$q-8$ $q-6$ $q-4$ $q-2$ q

Worksheet 4

Describing a Pattern

1   stacked some cans to form a pattern.

Pattern 1   Pattern 2   Pattern 3   Pattern 4

Fill in the blanks.

Pattern number	1	2	3	4	5	7	r
Number of cans	2	4	6	8	10	14	$r \times 2$

2 used matchsticks to form this pattern.

Pattern 1   Pattern 2   Pattern 3   Pattern 4

Help him find the number of matchsticks he needs to continue the pattern.

Pattern number	1	2	3	4	6	10	s
Number of matchsticks	6	12	18	24	30	60	$s \times 6$

Name: _____ Class: _____ Date: _____

Worksheet 5

Writing Algebraic Expressions

1 Write an algebraic expression to describe the rule.

(a)
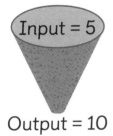
Input = 5

Output = 10

9

14

w

$w+5$

(b)
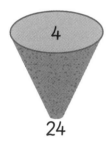
4

24

7

42

x

x *6 6x

(c)

15

3

40

8

y

$\frac{y}{5}$

(d)

13

9

11

7

z

z - 4

2 Write the algebraic expression in terms of *y*.

(a) 5 more than *y*

$y + 5$

(b) 4 less than *y*

$y - 4$

(c) 6 times *y*

$6y$

(d) half of *y*

$y \div 2$

3  baked *y* trays of cookies. baked 3 more trays of cookies than baked. Write an algebraic expression to show the number of trays of cookies baked.

$\cancel{6y} \cancel{} y + 3$

4 has *z* metal paper clips. She has twice as many paper clips as has. Write an algebraic expression to show the number of paper clips has.

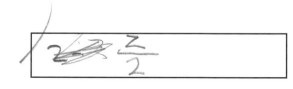 $\dfrac{z}{2}$

Worksheet 6

Writing and Evaluating Algebraic Expressions

1 A number machine changes the input number *w* to an output number *x* according to a rule.

(a)

Input *w*	8	9	10	4	15
Output *x*	16	18	20	8	30

Write an algebraic expression for *x* in terms of *w* to describe the rule used by the machine.

$$x = \cancel{w+} 2w$$

(b) Complete the table using the rule.

Input *w*	7	12	18	6
Output *x*	14	24	36	12

2 wrote a spreadsheet programme that changed the input number *k* using the rule $\dfrac{k}{5}$.

Complete the table using 's rule.

Input *k*	Output
5	1
10	2
35	7
100	20
45	9

Worksheet 7

Writing and Evaluating Algebraic Expressions

1   made these arrangements of some square tables and round stools.

  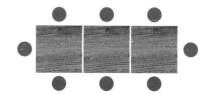

(a)   Complete the table.

Arrangement number	Number of tables, t	Number of stools, s
1	1	4
2	2	6
3	3	8
4	4	10
6	6	14

(b)   Write an expression for the number of stools s in terms of the number of tables t.

$$s = 2t + 2$$

(c)   Use your expression to find the value of s when $t = 12$.

26

2  stacked playing cards to make these arrangements (side view shown).

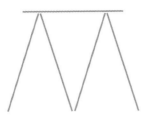 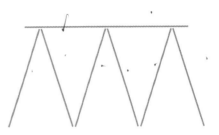

Arrangement 1   Arrangement 2   Arrangement 3

(a) Complete the table.

Arrangement number, n	Number of playing cards, c
1	2
2	5
3	8
5	~~11~~ 14
7	~~16~~ ~~17~~ 21

(b) Write an algebraic expression for the number of playing cards c in terms of the arrangement number n.

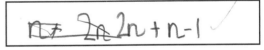

$c =$ ~~$2n$~~ ~~$2n$~~ $2n + n - 1$

(c) Evaluate your expression when $n = 11$.

32

Check that this answer is equal to the number of cards in Arrangement 11.

3 Evaluate each expression for the given values of n. In each case, write a formula for T in terms of n.

(a)

n	$4n+1$
1	5
2	9
3	13
4	17
5	21

(b)

n	$2n-2$
2	2
4	6
6	10
8	14
10	18

(c)

n	$3n+5$
1	8
2	11
10	35
20	65
99	302

294
× 3
297

Worksheet 8

Writing Formulae

1 Let T stand for the nth number in each pattern.

(a)

n	1	2	3	4	5
T	3	6	9	12	15

$T = 3n$

(b)

n	1	2	3	4	5
T	5	9	13	17	21

$T = 5n - n - 1$

(c)

n	1	2	3	4	5
T	5	7	9	11	13

6   7

$T = 2n + 3$

(d)

n	1	2	3	4	5
T	2	7	12	17	22

$T = 5n - 3$

2 The formula for the *n*th number in a sequence is:

$$2n + 4$$

(a) Find the 4th number.

12

(b) Find the 15th number.

34

(c) Find the 100th number.

204

(d) Find the sum of the first 10 numbers in the sequence.

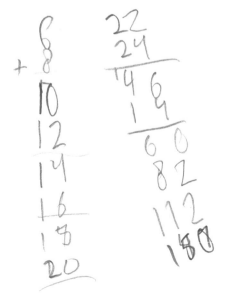

150

Worksheet 9

Using Formulae

1 The length of the longer side of a rectangle is x cm, which is 5 cm greater than the length of its shorter side. Its perimeter p cm is given by:

$$p = 4x - 10$$

(a) Find p when $x = 15$.

50

(b) Find p when $x = 28$.

$$\begin{array}{r} 3\,2\overset{3}{8} \\ \times\ 4 \\ \hline 112 \end{array}$$

102

(c) Find the length of the rectangle if the perimeter is 46 cm.

14

(d) Find the length of the rectangle if the perimeter is 95 cm.

95

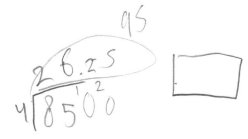

26.25

2 Use the formula $A = 72 + \dfrac{t}{2}$ to calculate the value of A:

(a) when $t = 12$

$A = 78$

(b) when $t = 38$

$A = 91$

(c) when $t = 75$

72
37
109 5

3
2)75

$A = 109.5$

(d) when $t = 18.7$

72
+ 9.35
81.35

09.35
2)18.70

$A = 81.35$

Name: ______________ Class: _____ Date: 5/3/20

Worksheet 10

Solving Equations

1 Find the value of y.

(a) $y + 2 = 43$

$y =$ 41

(b) $y + 34 = 70$

$y =$ 36

(c) $65 - y = 35$

$y =$ 30

(d) $4y = 80$

$y =$ 20

(e) $30 - 2y = 10$

$y = 10$

(f) $\dfrac{y}{18} = 0.5$

$y = 9$

(g) $\dfrac{24}{y} = 6$

$y = 4$

2 List all possible pairs of whole numbers a and b which solve this equation:

$a + b = 7$

a	b
0	7
1	6
2	5
3	4
4	3
5	2
6	1
7	0

Date: 5/3/20

 made a sequence of patterns using black and white triangles.

Pattern 1   Pattern 2   Pattern 3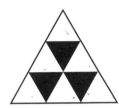

Pattern number	Number of black triangles	Number of white triangles	Total number of triangles
1	+1 (0	+2 (1	1
2	(1	(3	4
3	+2 (3	+3 (6	9
4	+3 (6	+4 (10	16
n	b = n	w =	t = n^2

Write algebraic expressions for the number of black triangles b, the number of white triangles w, and the total number of triangles t in terms of the pattern number n. Then, find the total number of triangles in Pattern 99.

Review 9

1 uses triangles and circles to form a sequence of patterns.

Pattern 1   Pattern 2   Pattern 3

(a) Complete the table.

Pattern number	Number of triangles	Number of circles
1	1	3
2	2	4
3		
7		
16		
a		

(b) Find the number of circles in Pattern 79.

2 wrote 10 consecutive whole numbers starting with *b*.

(a) What is the third number that he wrote? Write the number in terms of *b*.

[ ]

(b) What is the sixth number that he wrote? Write the number in terms of *b*.

[ ]

3 has a spreadsheet programme that uses a rule to change the input number *n*. Find an algebraic expression for the output *T* in terms of *n*.

n	28	8	12	4
T	7	2	3	1

[ ]

4 Evaluate the expression $5n + 2$ for the given values of *n*.

n	$5n + 2$
1	
2	
3	
6	
55	

5 *T* stands for the *n*th number in this pattern:

	1st	2nd	3rd	4th
	3	7	11	15

Write a formula for *T* in terms of *n*.

$T =$

6 Find each value of *k*.

(a) $5 + k = 20$

(b) $k - 12 = 46$

(c) $2k = 16$

(d) $\dfrac{35}{k} = 7$

7 Complete the table using the formula:

$$R = 12 + 0.8\,(x - 14)$$

x	R
20	
32	
54	
69	

8 ABC is a scalene triangle. AB is x cm, BC is three times the length of AB and AC is 4 cm longer than AB.

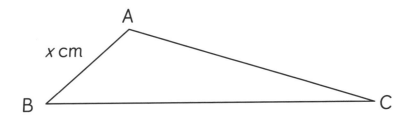

Write an algebraic expression in terms of x to describe:

(a)   the length of BC

(b)   the length of AC

(c)   the perimeter of triangle ABC

(d)   Use the formula $p = 5x + 4$ to calculate:

(i) p when $x = 5.5$

(ii) x when $p = 137$

Area and Perimeter

Chapter 10

Name: _____ Class: _____ Date: 11/3/20

Worksheet 1

Finding the Area and the Perimeter of Rectangles

1 Find the area and the perimeter of each rectangle.

(a)

8 cm

5 cm

area = 40 cm² ✓

perimeter = 26 cm ✓

(b)

16 cm

6 cm

area = 96 cm²

perimeter = 44 cm

(c)

9 cm

2.5 cm

area = 22.5 cm² ✓

perimeter = 23 cm ✓

(d)

3 cm

$7\frac{1}{3}$ cm

area = 22 cm² ✓

perimeter = $20\frac{2}{3}$ cm ✓

2 A rectangle has an area of 72 cm². Its longer side is 9 cm. What is its perimeter?

34 cm ✓

3 The perimeter of a rectangle is 63 cm. The length of its shorter side is 9 cm. Find the area of the rectangle.

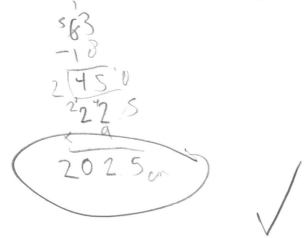

202.5 cm ✓

4 A rectangle has an area of 84 cm². Its longer side is 5 cm longer than its shorter side. Find its perimeter.

38 cm ✓

Name: _____ Class: _____ Date: 11/3/20

Worksheet 2

Finding the Area of Parallelograms

Find the area of each parallelogram.

(a)

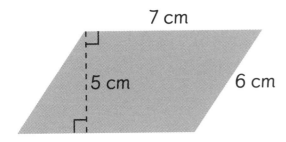

7 cm

5 cm

6 cm

area = 35_{un}^{2}

(b)

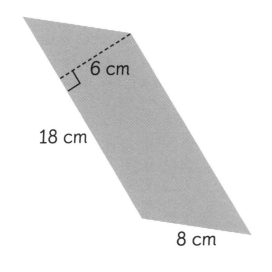

6 cm

18 cm

8 cm

$\begin{array}{r} 4 \\ 18 \\ \times\ 6 \\ \hline 108 \end{array}$

area = 108_{cm}^{2}

(c)

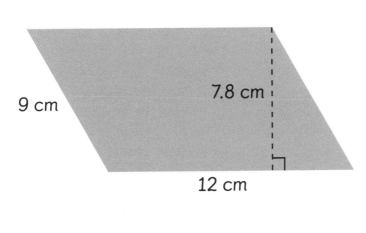

9 cm

7.8 cm

12 cm

$\begin{array}{r} 12 \\ \times\ 7.8 \end{array}$

area = 93.6_{cm}^{2}

$\begin{array}{r} 7.8 \\ \times\ 12 \\ \hline 15.6 \\ 78.0 \\ \hline 93.6 \end{array}$

Worksheet 3

Finding the Area of Triangles

Find the area of the shaded triangle in each figure.

(a)

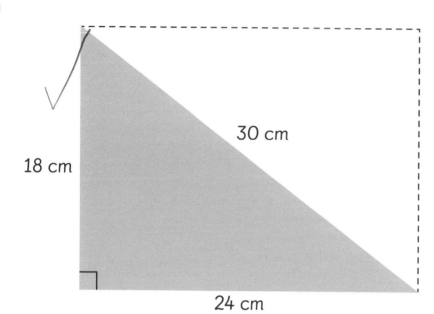

30 cm

18 cm

24 cm

$$\begin{array}{r} \overset{3}{2}4 \\ \times 18 \\ \hline 192 \\ 240 \\ \hline \end{array}$$

$$2\overline{)432}$$

$$216 \text{ cm}$$

(b)

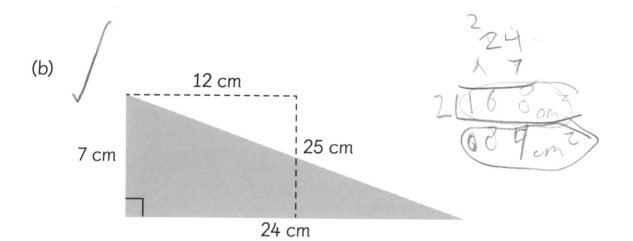

12 cm

7 cm

25 cm

24 cm

$$\begin{array}{r} \overset{2}{2}4 \\ \times 7 \\ \hline \end{array}$$

$$2\overline{)168 \text{ cm}}$$

$$084 \text{ cm}^2$$

(c)

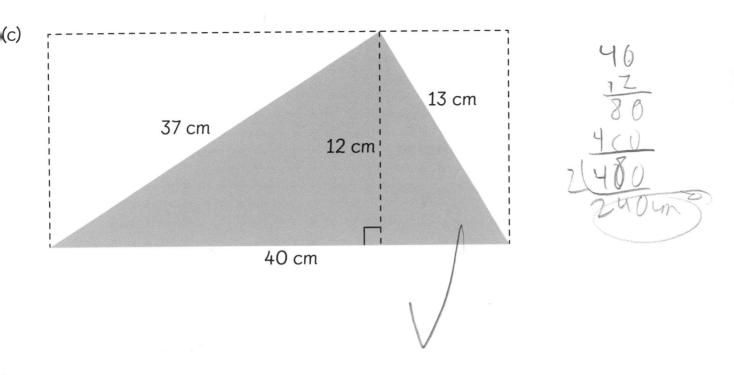

37 cm

13 cm

12 cm

40 cm

40
12
80
40
2 480
240 m²

(d)

17 cm

25 cm

15 cm

7.5 cm

28 cm

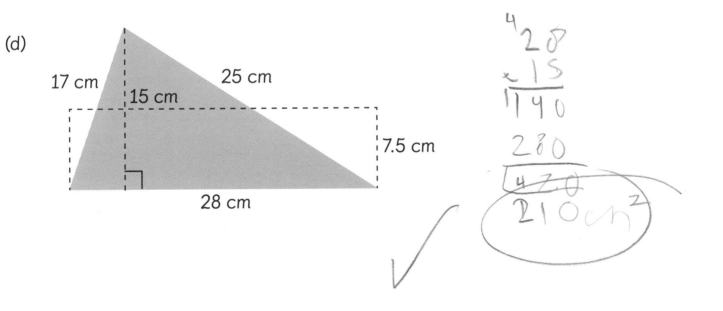

28
× 15
140
280
420
210 cm²

Worksheet 4

Finding the Area of Triangles

1 Find the area of each triangle.

(a)

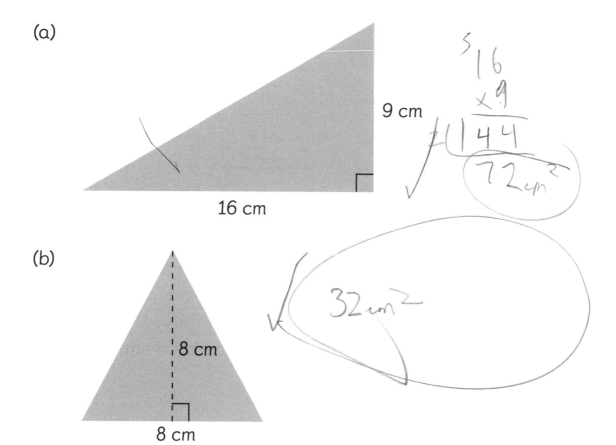

9 cm

16 cm

$^{5}16$
$\times 9$
144
$72\,cm^{2}$

(b)

8 cm

8 cm

$32\,cm^{2}$

(c)

15 cm

24 cm

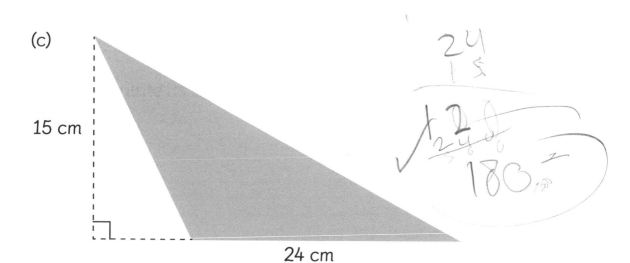

24
15
120
240
180

2 Find the area of each triangle by making the necessary measurements.

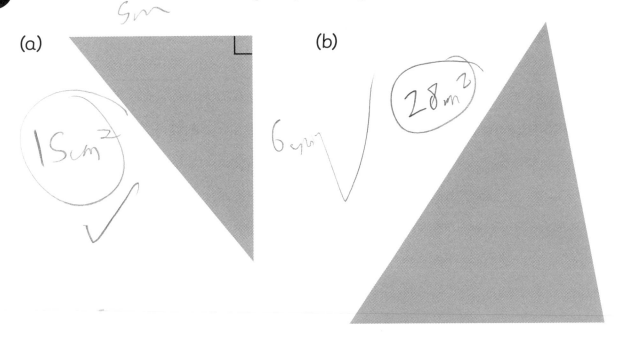

(a)

5cm

15cm² ✓

(b)

6cm

28m²

7cm

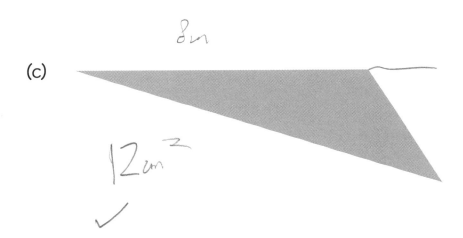

(c)

8m

12cm² ✓

Worksheet 5

Finding the Area of Triangles

1   uses this method to find the area of the shaded triangle.

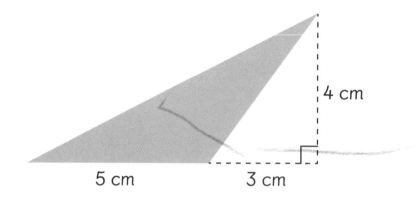

Area of unshaded triangle = $\dfrac{1}{2} \times 4 \times 3$

$= 6 \text{ cm}^2$

Area of whole triangle = $\dfrac{1}{2} \times 4 \times (5 + 3)$

$= 16 \text{ cm}^2$

Area of shaded triangle $= 16 - 6$

$= 10 \text{ cm}^2$

Make the necessary measurements and use  's method to find the area of each shaded triangle.

(a)

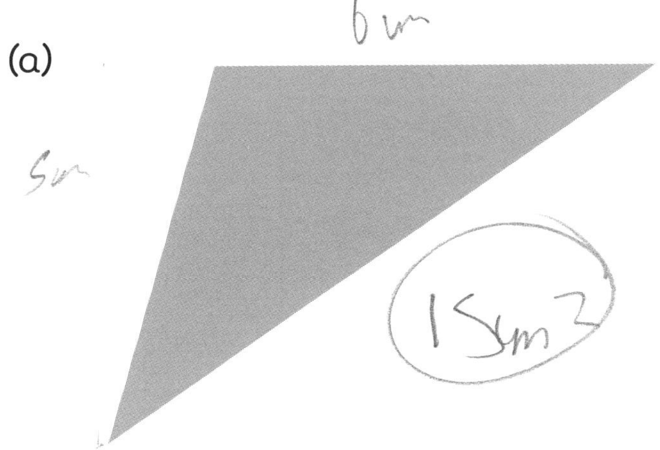

6 m

5 m

15 m²

(b)

244
24.5 cm²

14
7

2 uses this method to find the area of the triangle.

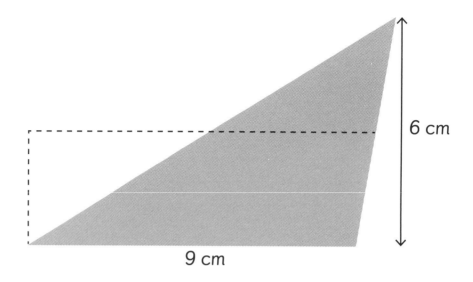

6 cm

9 cm

Height of rectangle = 6 ÷ 2
= 3 cm

Area of triangle = 3 × 9
= 27 cm²

Make the necessary measurements and use 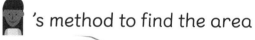 's method to find the area of the triangle below.

14 cm²

4 cm

Worksheet 6

Finding the Area of Parallelograms

1 Find the area of each parallelogram by making the necessary measurements.

(a)

5cm

~~18.5cm²~~

(33cm²)

(b)

36cm²

4

(c)

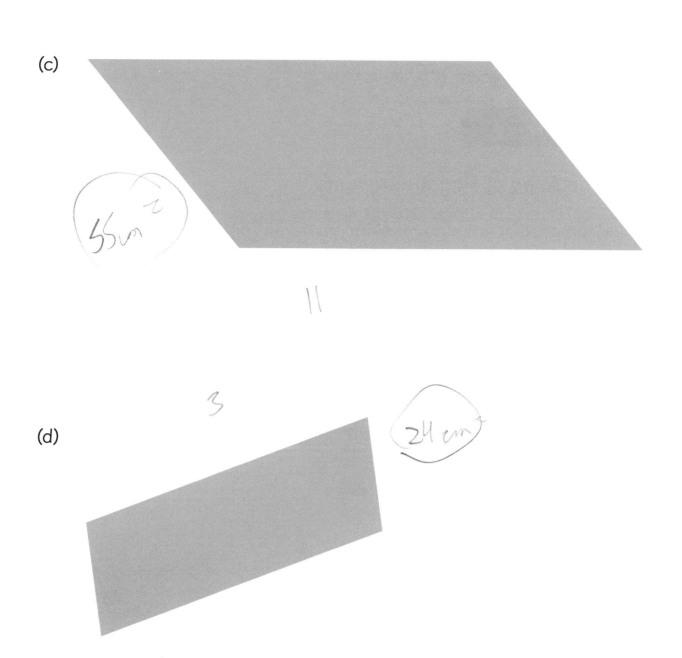

$55 cm^2$

11

3

(d)

$24 cm$

On the square grid, draw 8 different triangles, each with an area of 6 cm².

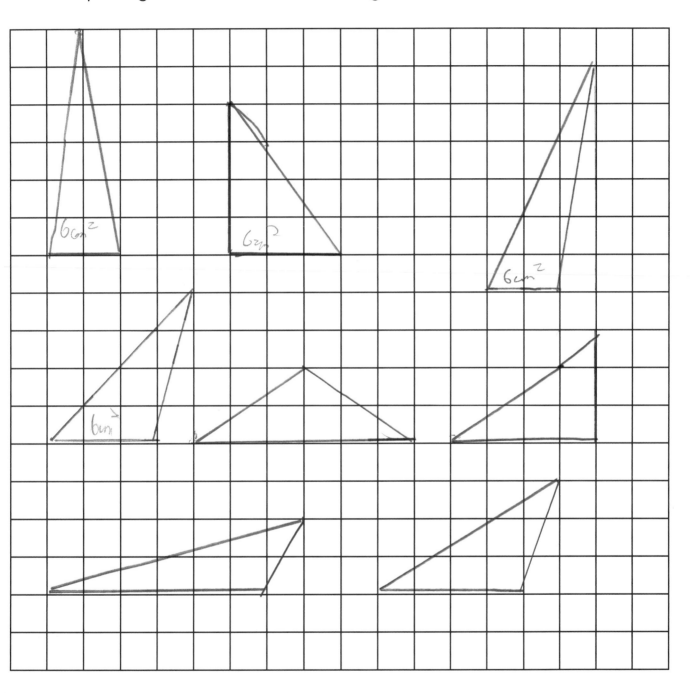

Measure the lengths of the sides of each triangle. Do the triangles have the same perimeter?

No

Review 10

1 Find the area and the perimeter of each figure.

(a)

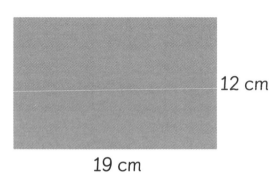

12 cm

19 cm

area = [ ]

perimeter = [ ]

(b)

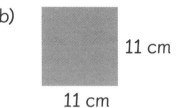

11 cm

11 cm

area = [ ]

perimeter = [ ]

(c)

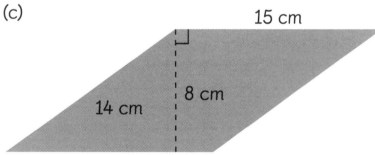

15 cm

8 cm

14 cm

area = [ ]

perimeter = [ ]

(d)

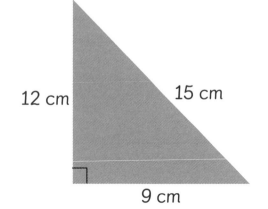

12 cm

15 cm

9 cm

area = [ ]

perimeter = [ ]

2 Find the area of each figure by making the necessary measurements.

(a)

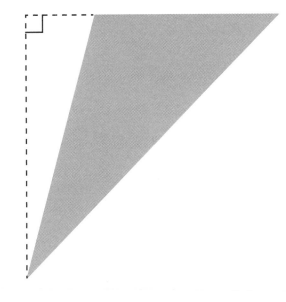

(b)

(c)

(d)

Revision 3

1 Write each ratio in its simplest form.

(a)   3 : 18   = [   ]

(b)   15 : 5   = [   ]

(c)   48 : 60   = [   ]

(d)   75 : 100   = [   ]

(e)   243 : 90   = [   ]

(f)   43 : 43   = [   ]

2 Evaluate the given expression for different values of n.

n	$100 - 6n$
1	
2	
3	
5	
11	

3 Write an algebraic expression for T in terms of k to describe a rule for this sequence.

Term number, k	1	2	3	4
Term, T	4	9	14	19

4 Find the value of x in each of the following equations.

(a) $9 + x = 14$

(b) $16 - x = 4$

(c) $x - 16 = 35$

(d) $3x = 21$

(e) $\dfrac{80}{x} = 16$

5 A florist has 480 individual flowers. The table shows how many of each type of flower she has.

Types of flowers	Percent
Roses	65%
Lilies	5%
Tulips	30%

(a)   The florist has ☐ roses.

(b)   The florist has ☐ tulips.

(c)   There are ☐ more tulips than lilies.

(d)   The original price of a bouquet of lilies was £32. The florist increased the price by 25%. What is the new price of a bouquet of lilies?

6 A Science Club has 108 members this year after a 20% increase in membership from last year. How many members did the club have last year?

	?

Last year: 20% | 20% | 20% | 20% | 20%

This year: 20% | 20% | 20% | 20% | 20% | 20%

7 The ratio of the number of male to the number of female passengers in a bus was 3 : 4. After 12 men got off the bus and 12 women got on, the ratio became 3 : 11. How many passengers were on the bus to begin with?

8 Find the area and the perimeter of each figure.

(a)

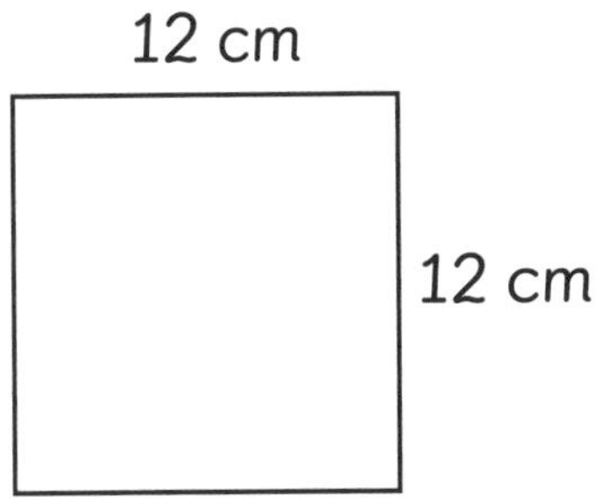

12 cm

12 cm

area   =

perimeter =

(b)

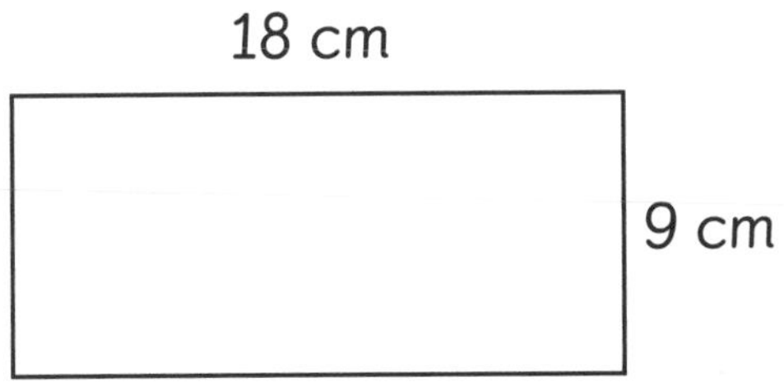

18 cm

9 cm

area   =

perimeter =

(c)

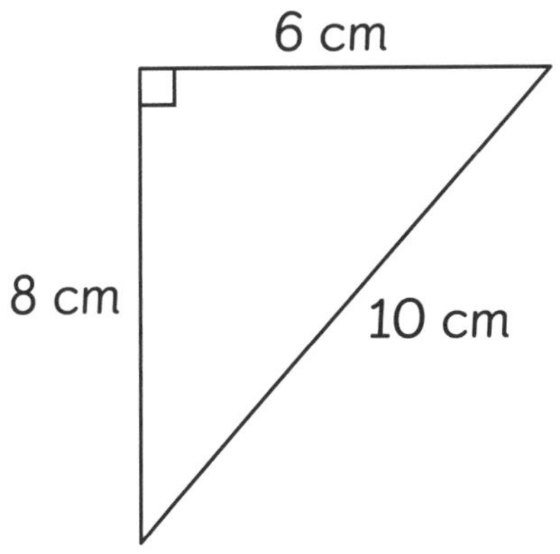

6 cm

8 cm

10 cm

area   =

perimeter =

(d)

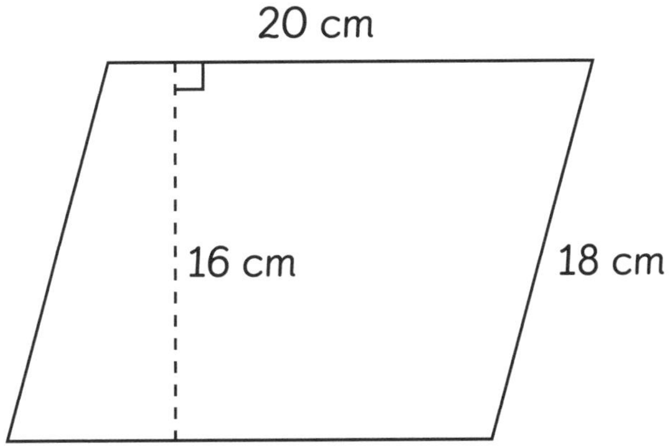

20 cm

16 cm

18 cm

area   =

perimeter =

9 Find the side length and the perimeter of each square.

(a)

Area = 81 cm²

(b)

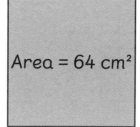

Area = 64 cm²

side length = _____

perimeter = _____

side length = _____

perimeter = _____

10 A rectangle has a perimeter of 68 cm. Its shorter side is 12 cm shorter than its longer side.

(a) Find the length of its longer side and the length of its shorter side.

(b) Calculate its area.

Volume

Chapter 11

Name: _____ Class: _____ Date: _____

Worksheet 1

Finding the Volume of Cubes and Cuboids

1 The volume of each small cube is 1 cm³. Find the volume of each cuboid.

(a)

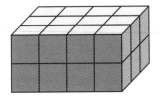

Volume = [ ]

(b)

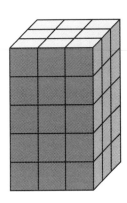

Volume = [ ]

(c)

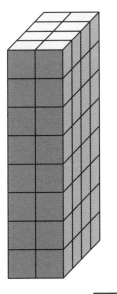

Volume = [ ]

(d)

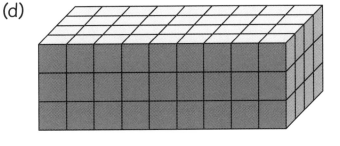

Volume = [ ]

The volume of each small cube is 1 cm³. Find the volume of each cube.

(a)

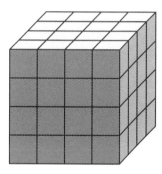

Volume =

(b)

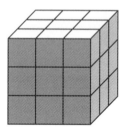

Volume =

(c)

Volume =

(d)

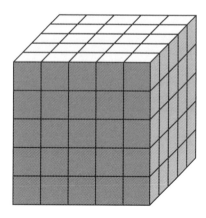

Volume =

Name: _____ Class: _____ Date: _____

Finding the Volume of Cubes and Cuboids

1 Find the volume of each cuboid.

(a)

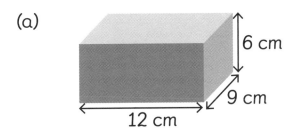

6 cm

9 cm

12 cm

(b)

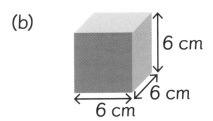

6 cm

6 cm

6 cm

(c)

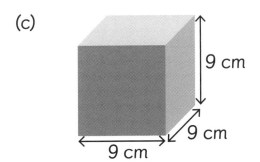

9 cm

9 cm

9 cm

(d)

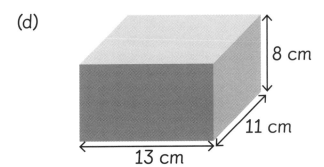

8 cm

11 cm

13 cm

2 Four cuboid bricks are stacked as shown. Each brick has two square faces. Find the volume of each brick.

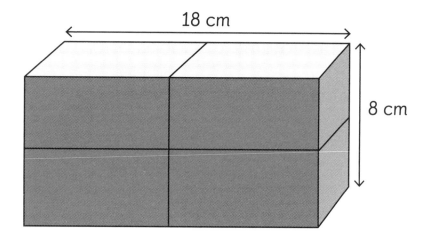

18 cm

8 cm

Name: _____ Class: _____ Date: _____

Finding the Volume of Cubes and Cuboids

1 Find the volume of each cuboid.

(a)

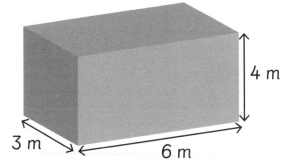

4 m

3 m

6 m

(b)

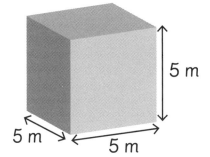

5 m

5 m

5 m

(c)

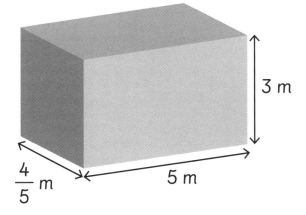

3 m

$\frac{4}{5}$ m

5 m

(d)

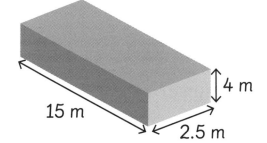

4 m

15 m

2.5 m

2 Find the volume of each figure and answer the questions.

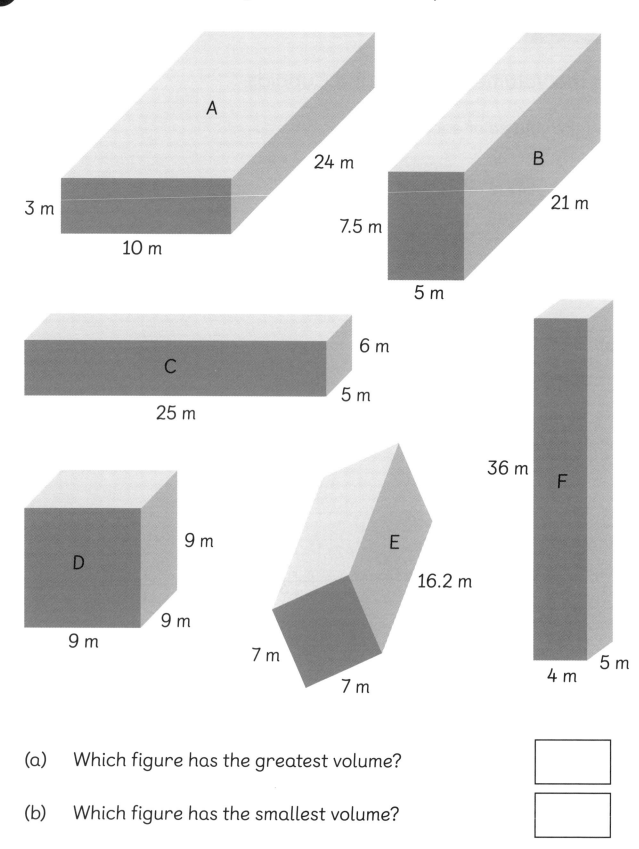

A

24 m

3 m

10 m

B

21 m

7.5 m

5 m

C

6 m

5 m

25 m

D

9 m

9 m

9 m

E

16.2 m

7 m

7 m

36 m

F

5 m

4 m

(a)   Which figure has the greatest volume?

(b)   Which figure has the smallest volume?

Name: _____ Class: _____ Date: _____

Worksheet 4

Finding the Volume of Cubes and Cuboids

Find the volume of each cuboid.

(a)

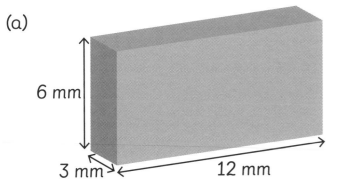

6 mm

3 mm   12 mm

(b)

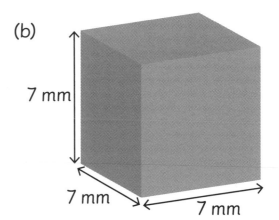

7 mm

7 mm   7 mm

(c)

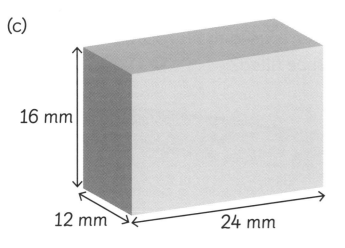

16 mm

12 mm   24 mm

(d)

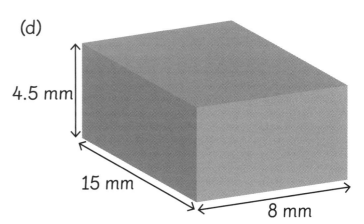

4.5 mm

15 mm   8 mm

Worksheet 5

Solving Problems Involving the Volume of Solids

1 A cuboid of pure chocolate is melted and made into chocolate cubes with 2-cm sides. How many chocolate cubes can be made?

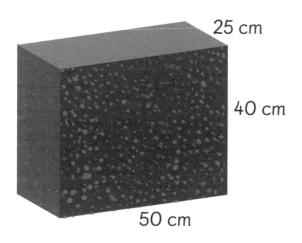

25 cm

40 cm

50 cm

2 Before a cycling competition, a rectangular tank (as shown below) is filled to the brim with drinking water. The water is used to fill 750-cm³ bottles for the participants. How many bottles can be filled?

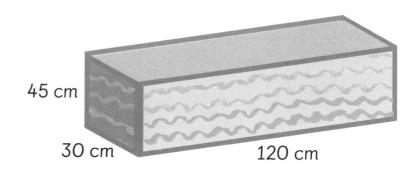

45 cm

30 cm

120 cm

3 A cuboidal block of soap is cut into smaller cubes with 5-cm sides. What is the greatest number of cubes that can be cut from this block of soap?

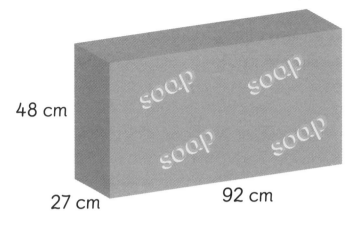

48 cm

27 cm

92 cm

4 An empty tank and a bucket are shown below. How many buckets full of water are needed to fill the tank up to the brim?

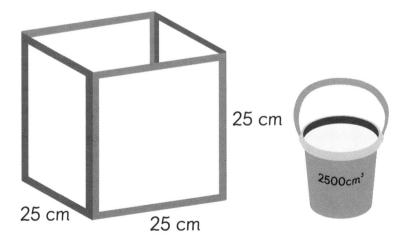

25 cm

25 cm

25 cm

2500cm³

Date:_____

A metal cube is melted down and made into three cubes of different sizes. The side length of each cube is a whole number. Find the smallest possible volume of the original cube.

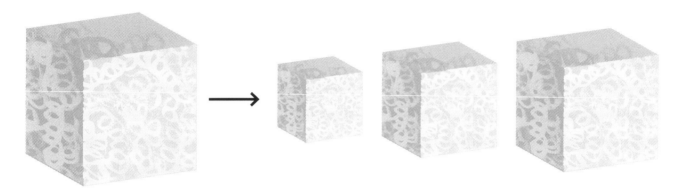

Review 11

1 Find the volume of each cuboid.

(a)

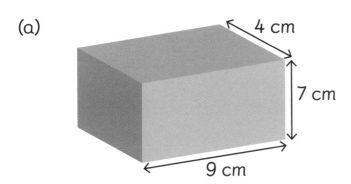

(b)

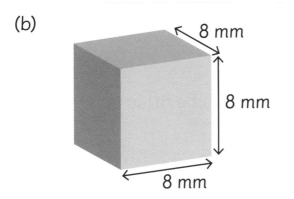

(c)

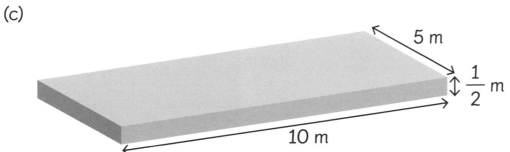

(d)

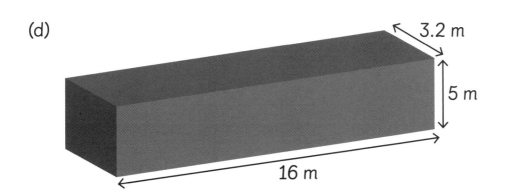

2 At a factory, a 1-metre cube of sponge is cut into smaller cubes with 8-cm sides. What is the greatest number of smaller cubes that can be cut from the large sponge cube?

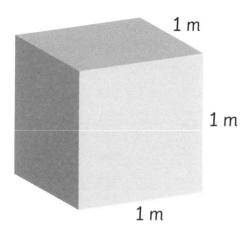

1 m

1 m

1 m

3 Find the largest number of 3-cm cubes that can be fitted into the box shown below.

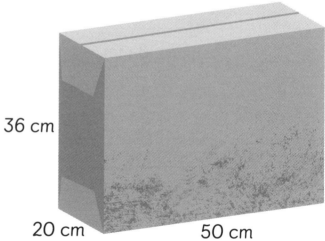

36 cm

20 cm

50 cm

Geometry

Name: _____ Class: _____ Date: _____

Worksheet 1

Investigating Vertically Opposite Angles

1 Find pairs of equal angles.

(a)

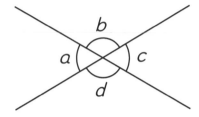

∠⬜ = ∠⬜

∠⬜ = ∠⬜

(b)

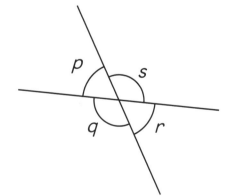

∠⬜ = ∠⬜

∠⬜ = ∠⬜

2 Find the unknown angles.

(a)

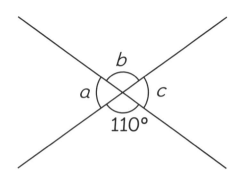

∠a = ⬚

∠b = ⬚

∠c = ⬚

(b)

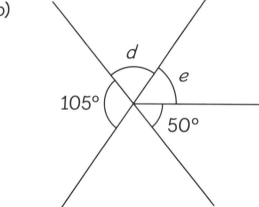

∠d = ⬚

∠e = ⬚

(c)

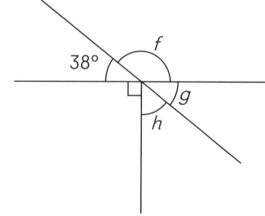

∠f = ⬚

∠g = ⬚

∠h = ⬚

Name: _____ Class: _____ Date: _____

Worksheet 2

Solving Problems Involving Angles

1 The ratio of the value of $\angle a$ to the value of $\angle b$ is 2 : 1. Find $\angle a$, $\angle b$ and $\angle c$.

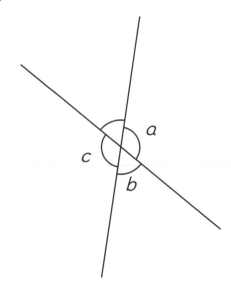

$\angle a = $ ⬚

$\angle b = $ ⬚

$\angle c = $ ⬚

2 The ratio of the value of $\angle d$ to the value of $\angle e$ is 3 : 5. Find $\angle d$, $\angle e$ and $\angle f$.

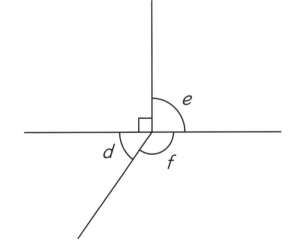

$\angle d = $ ⬚

$\angle e = $ ⬚

$\angle f = $ ⬚

3 The ratio of the value of ∠g to the value of ∠h is 2 : 7. Find ∠g , ∠h , ∠j and ∠k

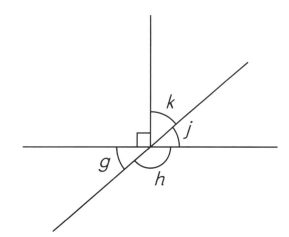

∠g = ☐

∠h = ☐

∠j = ☐

∠k = ☐

4 The ratio of the value of ∠n to the value of ∠m is 6 : 5. Find ∠l , ∠m and ∠n.

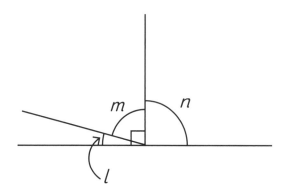

∠l = ☐

∠m = ☐

∠n = ☐

5 The ratio ∠p : ∠q : ∠r is 5 : 3 : 1. Find the value of ∠p , ∠q and ∠r.

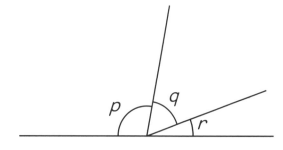

∠p = ☐

∠q = ☐

∠r = ☐

Worksheet 3

Investigating Angles in Triangles

1 Find the value of ∠x in each triangle.

(a)

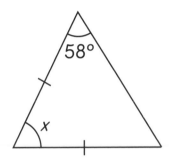

(b)

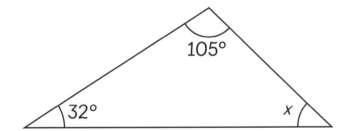

(c)

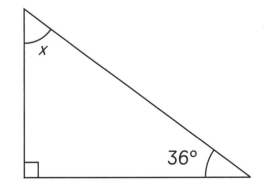

2 Find ∠ABC.

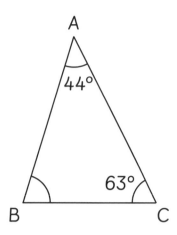

3 Find ∠DFE.

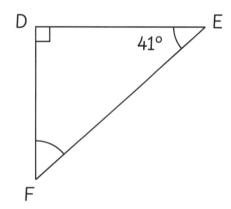

4 Find ∠GHI and ∠HGI.

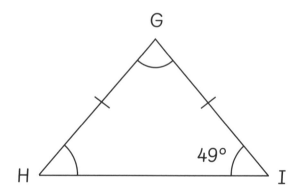

Worksheet 4

Investigating Angles in Quadrilaterals

1 Find the value of the unknown angles.

(a)

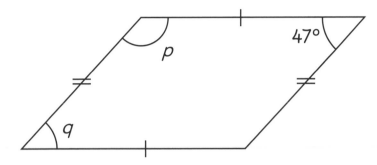

(b)

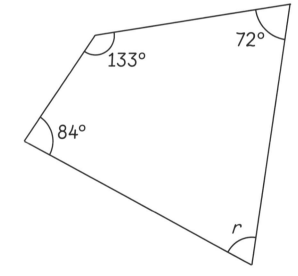

(c)

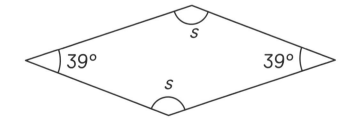

2 Find ∠ABC.

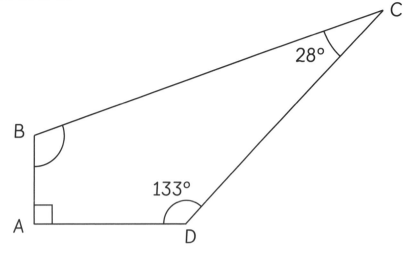

3 Find ∠EFG.

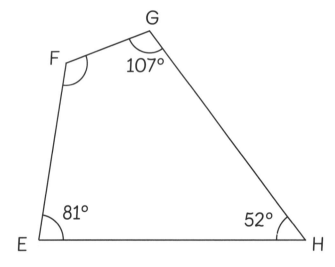

4 In quadrilateral KLMN, ∠KLM = ∠LMN. Find ∠LMN.

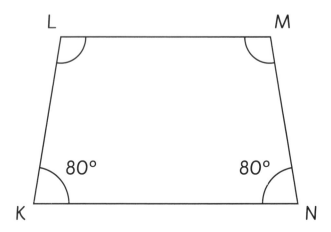

Worksheet 5

Solving Problems Involving Angles in Triangles and Quadrilaterals

1 This figure is made up of two equilateral triangles. Find $\angle a + \angle b + \angle c + \angle d$.

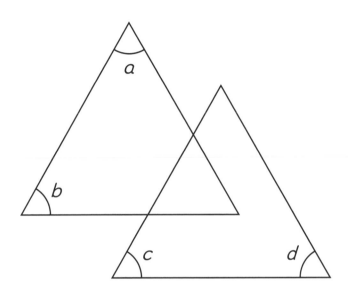

2 Find $\angle p + \angle q + \angle r + \angle s + \angle t + \angle u + \angle v$.

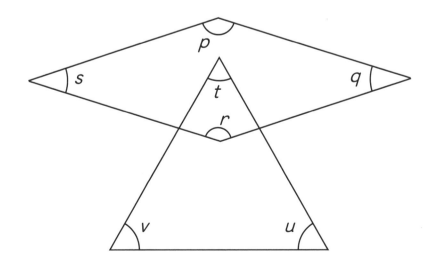

3 In octagon ABCDEFGH, all the sides are of equal length and all the angles are equal. Find the value of ∠AHB.

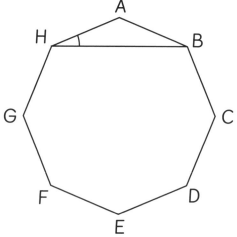

Worksheet 6

Naming Parts of a Circle

 The centre of each circle is shown. Measure and write down the length of the radius and the length of the diameter of each circle.

(a)

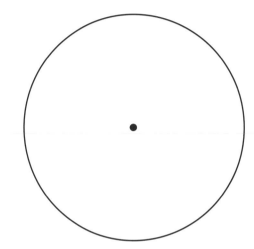

(b)

(c)

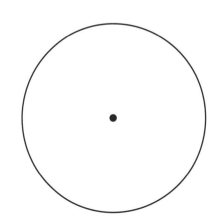

2 Given the diameter of each circle, state its radius.

(a)

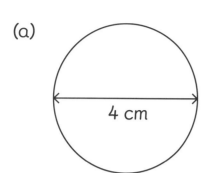

4 cm

(b)

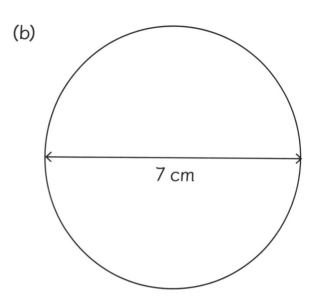

7 cm

3 The radius of each circle is given. State its diameter.

(a)

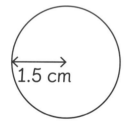

1.5 cm

(b)

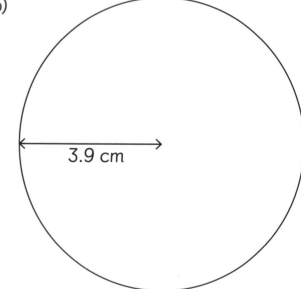

3.9 cm

Worksheet 7

Solving Problems Involving Angles in a Circle

1 O is the centre of each circle.

(a) Find $\angle a$.

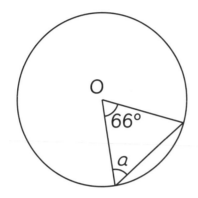

(b) Find $\angle b$.

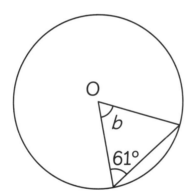

(c) The ratio of $\angle c$ to $\angle d$ is $2 : 3$. Find $\angle c$ and $\angle d$.

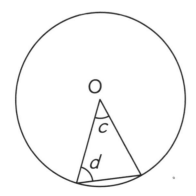

2 O is the centre of the circle and the ratio of ∠e to ∠f is 3 : 4. Find ∠e and ∠f.

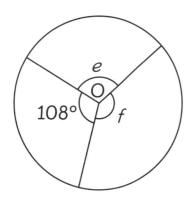

3 O is the centre of the circle. Given that ∠JOL = 106°, find ∠OLK.

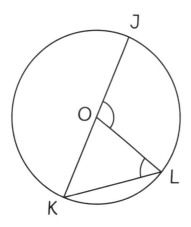

4 O is the centre of the circle and the ratio of ∠q to ∠p is 2 : 7. Find ∠p, ∠q and ∠r.

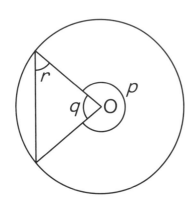

Worksheet 8

Drawing Quadrilaterals

1 In parallelogram ABCD, the sides AB, DC are 4 cm apart and the sides AD, BC are 8 cm apart. Draw the parallelogram ABCD.

2 Draw a square and a rectangle, where the perimeter of the square is the same as the perimeter of the rectangle.

3 Draw three different trapeziums whose parallel sides are 6 cm apart.

4 Draw a rhombus where the length of each side is 5 cm.

Name: ________________ Class: _____ Date: __________

Worksheet 9

Drawing Triangles

1 In triangle ABC, the length of AB is 7 cm, ∠CAB = 50° and ∠CBA = 80°. Draw the triangle ABC.

(a) Measure the length of:

(i) AC

(ii) BC

(b) Measure ∠ACB.

(c) What kind of triangle is this?

2 In triangle DEF, the length of EF is 6 cm, ∠DEF = 40° and ∠DFE = 40°.
In triangle GHI, the length of GH is 8 cm, ∠GHI = 30° and ∠HGI = 45°.
Draw triangles DEF and GHI.

(a) Measure the perimeter of:

    (i) triangle DEF

    (ii) triangle GHI

(b) Measure the value of:

    (i) ∠FDE

    (ii) ∠GIH

(c) Find the area of triangle DEF, to the nearest cm².

Worksheet 10

Drawing Triangles

1 By making the necessary measurements, find the ratio of the two marked lengths.

(a)

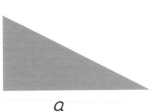

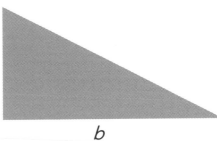

a

b

The ratio of a : b = ⬚ .

(b)

c

d

The ratio of c : d = ⬚ .

2 The triangles below are similar.

(a)

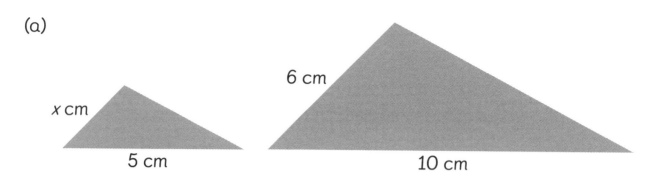

Find the value of x.

(b)

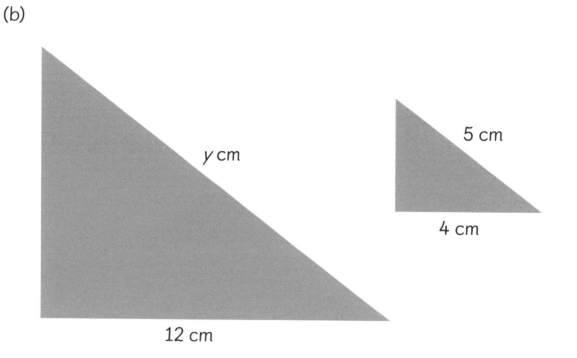

Find the value of y.

Worksheet 11

Drawing Nets of Three-Dimensional Shapes

1 Match.

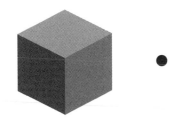

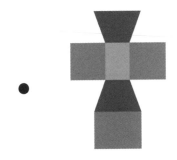

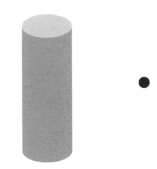

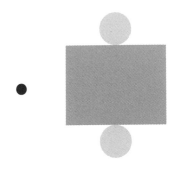

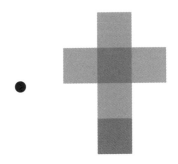

2 The figure below shows a pentagonal prism.

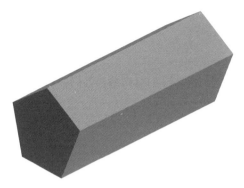

(a)   How many flat faces are there?

(b)   Name the shapes of the flat faces and the number of each type.

(c)   Draw a net of the prism.

Worksheet 12

Drawing Nets of Three-Dimensional Shapes

Two square pyramids are shown below.

 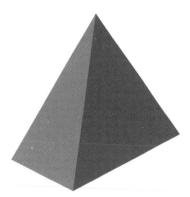

(a) Draw two different nets for each figure.

(b) List two differences between the square pyramids.

Date:_____

Find the sum of $\angle p$, $\angle q$, $\angle r$, $\angle s$ and $\angle t$. Show two different ways to obtain the answer.

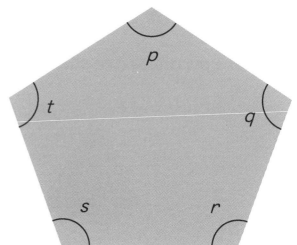

Review 12

1 The ratio of the value of ∠b to the value of ∠c is 1 : 4. Find ∠a, ∠b, ∠c and ∠d.

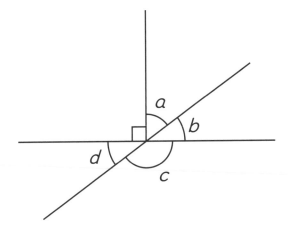

2 The value of ∠f is twice that of ∠e. Find ∠e, ∠f and ∠g.

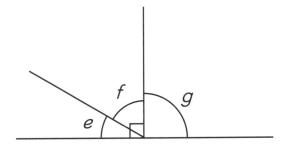

3 Find ∠JKL.

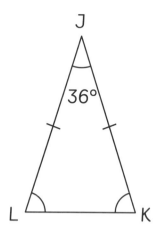

4 The ratio of ∠MPO to ∠MNO is 1 : 4. Find ∠MPO and ∠MNO.

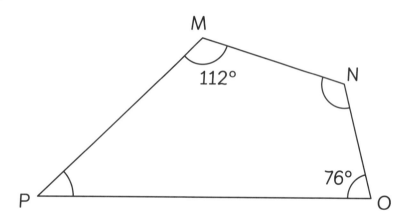

5 Find ∠p + ∠q + ∠r + ∠s + ∠t + ∠u + ∠v + ∠w + ∠x + ∠y.

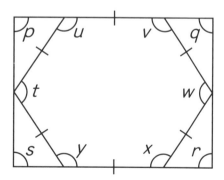

6 O is the centre of the circle. Given that ∠OYZ = 53°, find ∠XOZ.

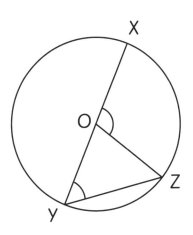

7 In triangle ABC, AB = 6 cm, AC = 3 cm and ∠CAB = 85°. Triangle DEF is similar to triangle ABC and the ratio of the lengths of AB : DE = 2 : 1. Draw the triangles ABC and DEF.

8 Two figures are shown below.

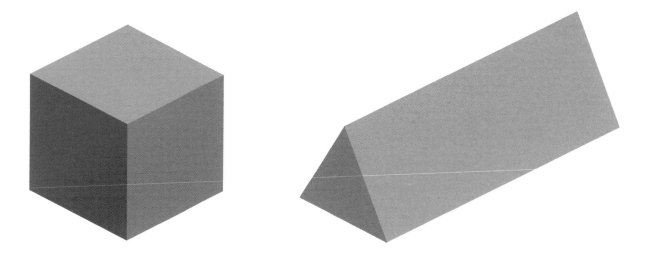

Draw two different nets for each figure.

Position and Movement

Chapter 13

Name: _____ Class: _____ Date: _____

Worksheet 1

Showing Negative Numbers

1 This ruler shows the water level of a river during a drought in the month of June.

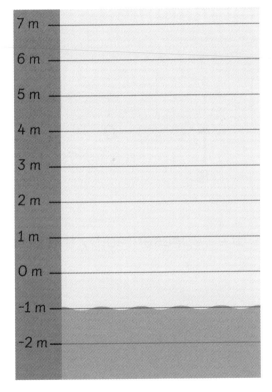

(a) In the month of July, the water level increased by 6 metres. Shade to show the new water level. What was the water level in July?

(b) In August, the water level dropped. The difference in the water level between July and August was 4 m. Find the difference between the water level in June and the water level in August.

2 Mark and label the given numbers on each number line.

(a) −3 and 1

0

(b) 0 and −7

−2

3

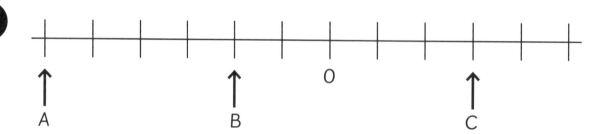

0

A   B   C

(a) What numbers are represented by the points A, B and C?

A :

B :

C :

(b) Find the difference between:

(i) the value of A and B

(ii) the value of A and C

Worksheet 2

Describing Position

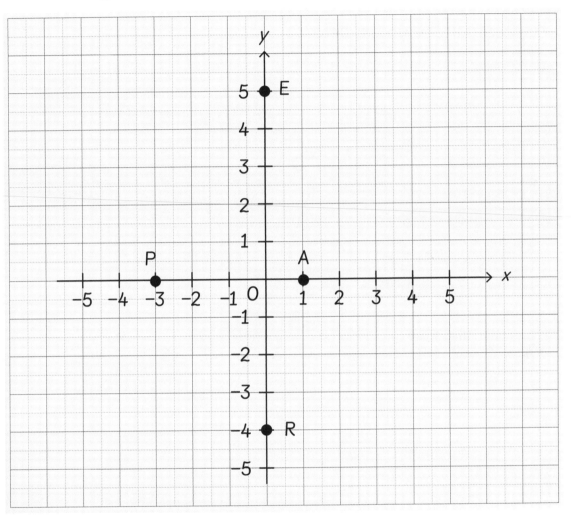

1 What are the coordinates:

(a)   of point P

(b)   of point E

(c)   of point A

(d)   of point R

2 Point L is at (0, 0) and point S is at (0, –2). Label points L and S on the graph.

Worksheet 3

Describing Position

1 A kite ABCD is shown in the graph below.

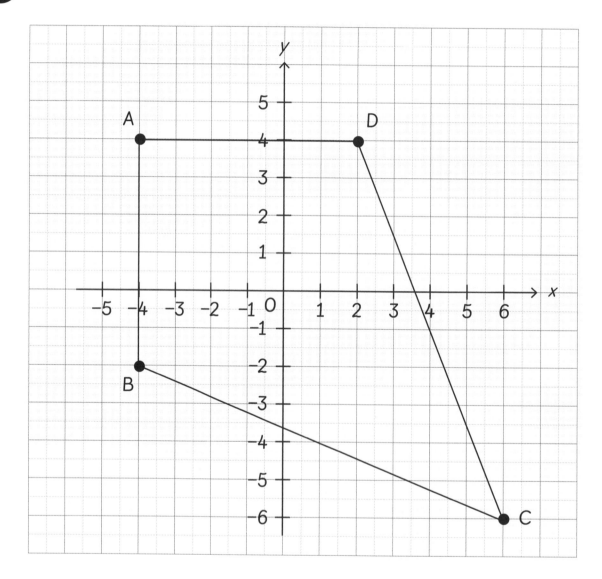

(a) Write the coordinates:

    (i)   of point A

    (ii)   of point B

    (iii) of point C

    (iv)   of point D

(b) Point E is such that quadrilateral ABED is a square. What are the
     coordinates of point E?

(c) Point F is such that triangle BFC is a right-angle triangle. Write one
     possible pair of coordinates of point F.

(d) Point G is at (–2, 6). What is the shape of quadrilateral AGDB?

2

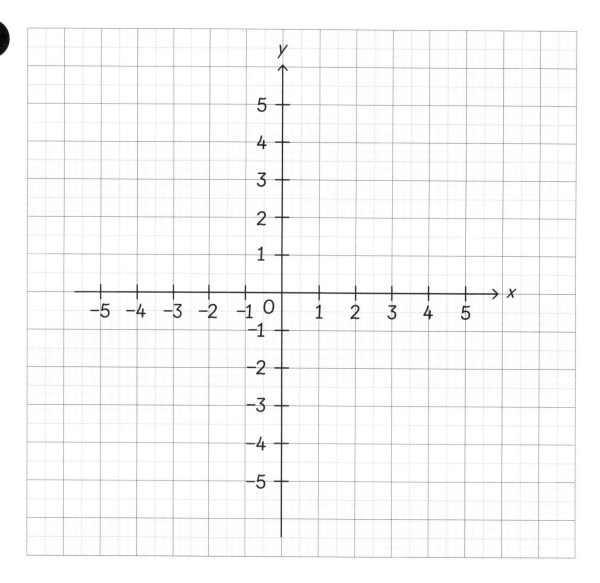

(a)　The coordinates of some points are:

　　P (−2 , 2)　　　　Q (−2 , −2)　　　　R (2 , −2)　　　　S (2 , 2)

　　Draw and label the points on the graph.

(b)　State the shape of the quadrilateral PQRS.

(c)　Point T is below the line QR, such that the area of triangle TQR is half
　　the area of PQRS. Write the coordinates of a possible point T.

Worksheet 4

Drawing Polygons on a Coordinate Grid

1 The coordinates of the vertices of some polygons are given. Draw and name each polygon.

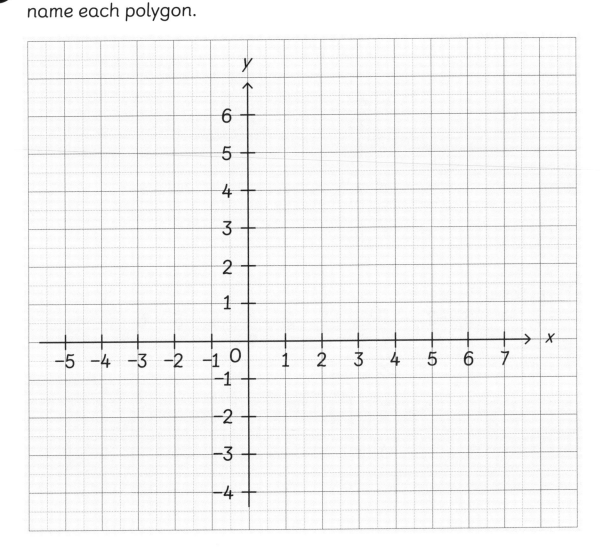

(a) A(–1, 4) B(–1, 6) C(–3, 6) D(–3, 4)

ABCD is a [   ] .

(b) E(0, 1) F(6, 4) G(6, 1)

EFG is a [   ] .

(c)   J(–1, 8)   K(6, 8)   L(7, 5)   M(0, 5)

JKLM is a [   ].

(d)   P(1, –2)   Q(–3, –4)   R(–5, 0)   S(–3, 1)

PQRS is a [   ].

2 WXYZ is a rhombus.

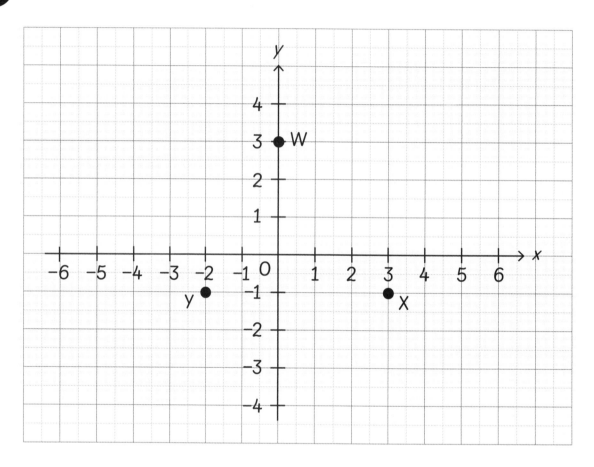

Write down the coordinates of point Z and draw the rhombus.

The coordinates of point Z are ([   ] , [   ]).

Worksheet 5

Describing Translations

Some rectangles are shown on the grid below.

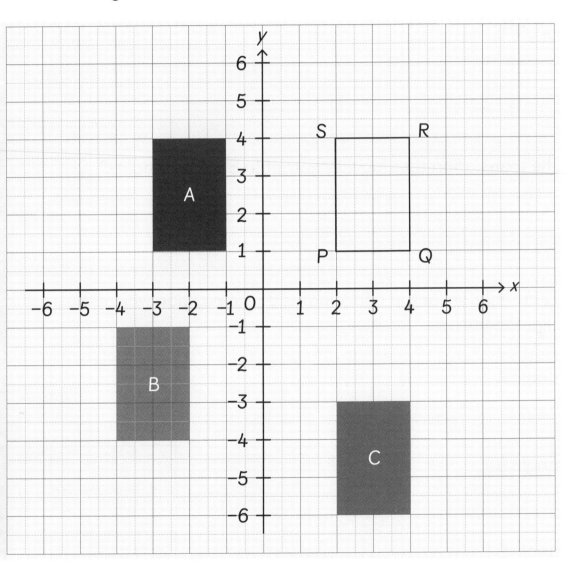

Lulu describes how she moves rectangle PQRS to the position of rectangle A.

Translate 5 units to the left

1 Describe the translation that moves rectangle PQRS to each of the following positions. Use Lulu's description to help you.

(a)   rectangle B

(b)   rectangle C

2 Describe the translation that moves rectangle B to rectangle C.

3 For each rectangle, write the coordinates of the position where the original point R ends up.

(a)   rectangle A

(b)   rectangle B

(c)   rectangle C

Name: _____ Class: _____ Date: _____

Worksheet 6

Describing Reflections

Draw the image of each figure.

1

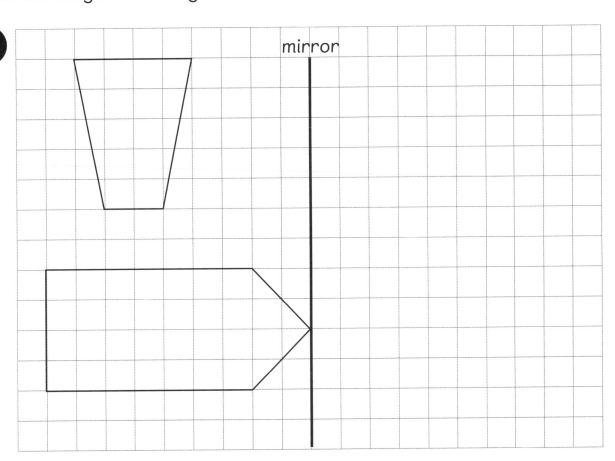

mirror

2

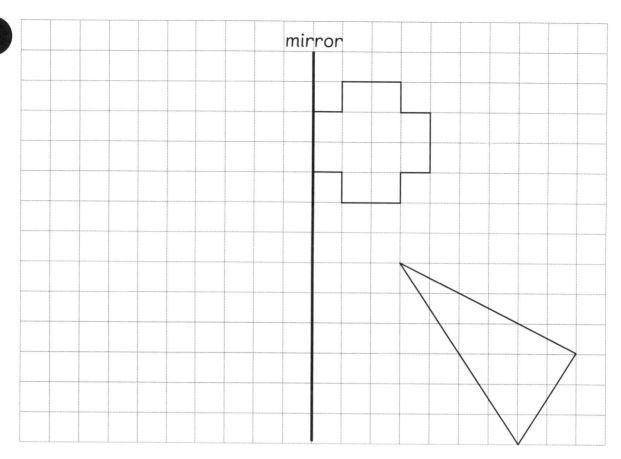

3

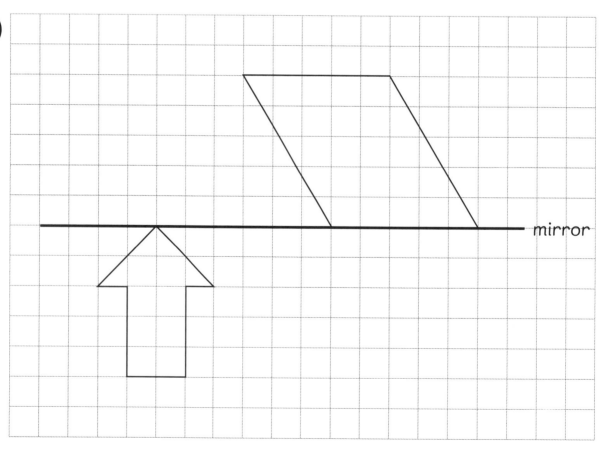

Name: _____ Class: _____ Date: _____

Worksheet 7

Describing Movements

Draw to show ABCD when it is reflected in the *x*-axis and in the *y*-axis.

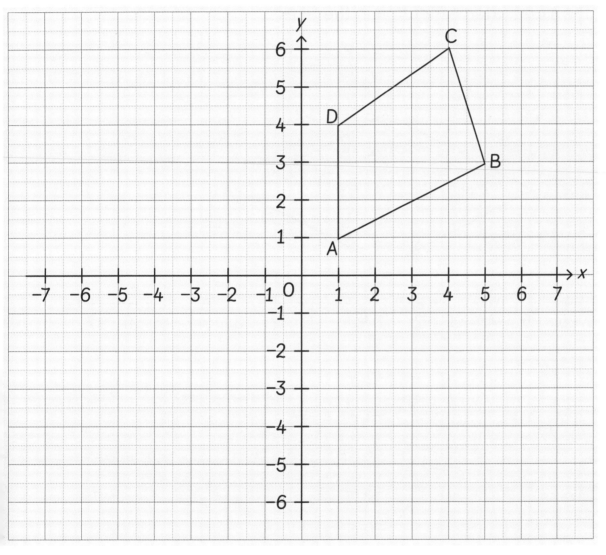

Complete the table to show the coordinates of each point after reflection.

	reflect in *x*-axis	reflect in *y*-axis
A(1, 1)		
B(5, 3)		
C(4, 6)		
D(1, 4)		

Worksheet 8

Describing Movements

1 Complete the table to show the position of each point after translation 6 units down and after reflection in the *x*-axis.

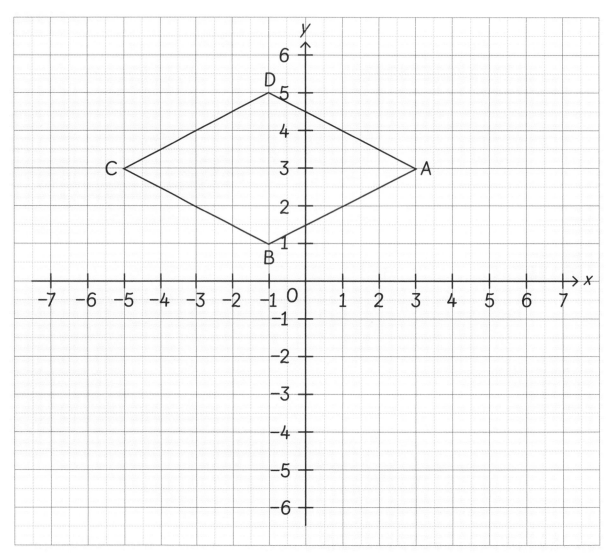

point	coordinates	after translation	after reflection
A	(3, 3)	(3, −3)	(3, −3)
B			
C			
D			

2 Complete the table to show the position of each point after translation and after reflection.

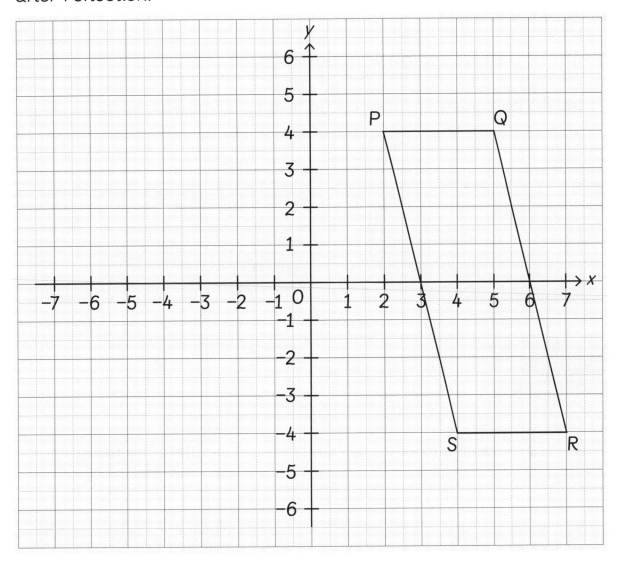

point	coordinates	after translation	after reflection
P	(2, 4)	(−2 , 4)	(−2, 4)
Q			
R			
S			

Is the position of the shape after reflection the same as it is after translation? Explain your answer.

Worksheet 9

Using Algebra to Describe Position

1 The sides of square ABCD are 4 units long. Complete the table.

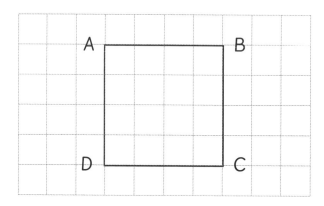

point	A	B	C	D
coordinates	(m, n)			

2 The sides of square EFGH are 7 units long. Complete the table.

point	E	F	G	H
coordinates	(10, p)			

3 In rectangle JKLM, the coordinates of K are $(s, t+5)$. Complete the table.

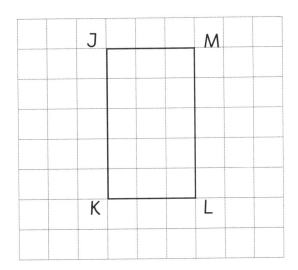

point	J	K	L	M
coordinates		$(s, t+5)$		

4 The sides of rectangle PQRS are 12 cm long and 4 cm long. Complete the table.

point	P	Q	R	S
coordinates	(x, y)			

Worksheet 10

Using Algebra to Describe Movements

1 Triangle ABC is reflected in the *x*-axis and in the *y*-axis.

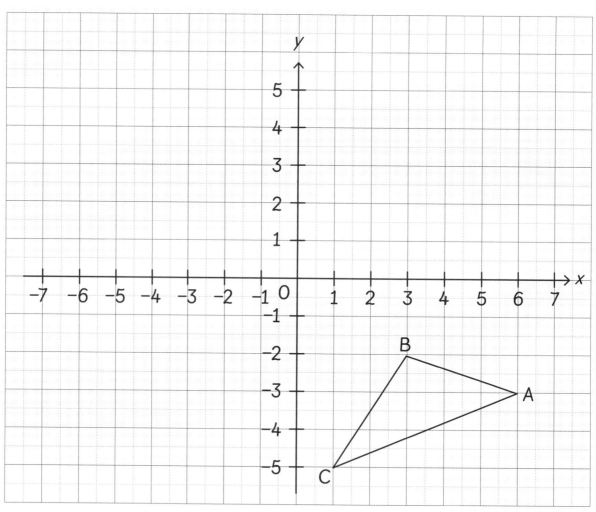

Given that point X is any point on the triangle, complete the table.

point	coordinates	after reflection in *x*-axis	after reflection in *y*-axis
A			
B			
C			
X	(x, y)		

2 Trapezium PQRS is translated.

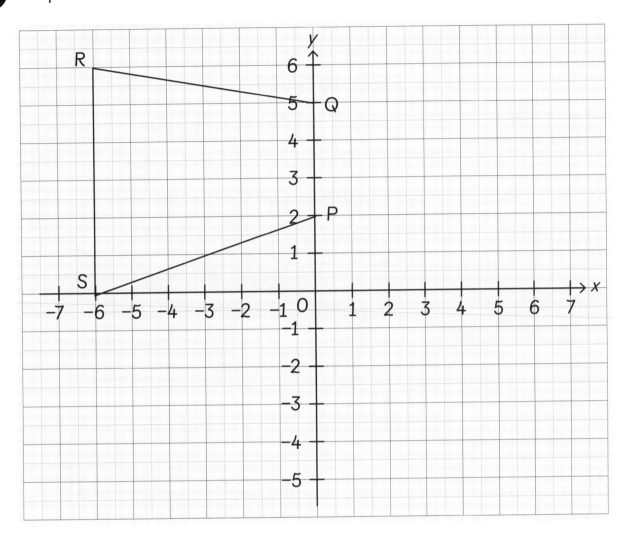

Given that point Y is any point on the trapezium, complete the table.

point	coordinates	after translation
P		(4, −3)
Q		
R		
S		
Y	(x, y)	

Date:_____

When some shapes undergo a reflection, they end up at the same overall position as they do after a translation.

Is this possible for:

(a)   a rectangle?

(b)   a parallelogram?

If it is possible, show an example by drawing on the grid below.

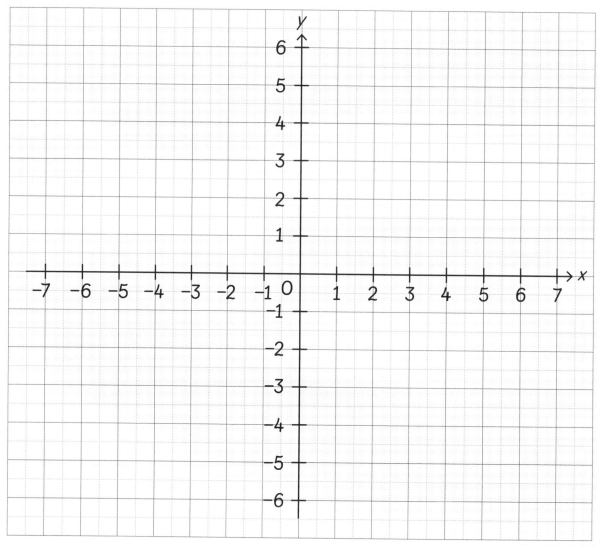

Describe the reflection and the translation.

Review 13

1 Find the difference between the values of A and B.

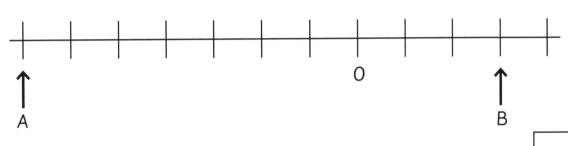

2

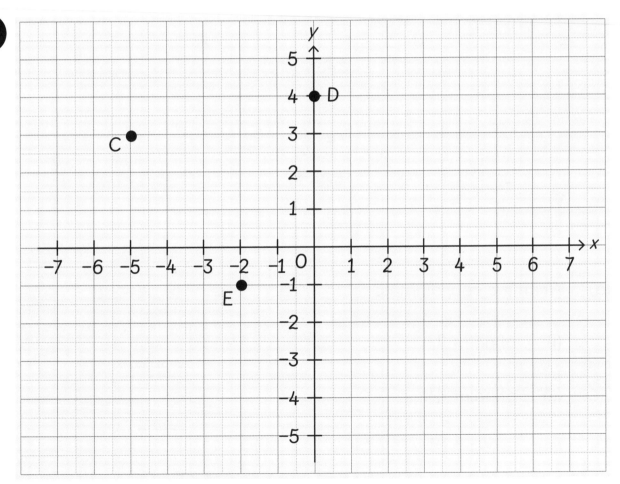

Write the coordinates:

(a) of point C [ ]

(b) of point D [ ]

(c) of point E [ ]

3 JKLM is a parallelogram.

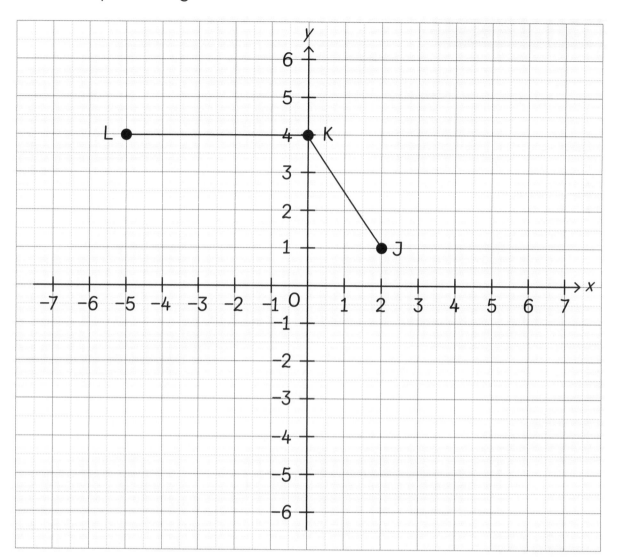

(a) Write the coordinates:

(i) of point J

(ii) of point K

(iii) of point L

(b) What are the coordinates of point M?

(c) Complete the parallelogram.

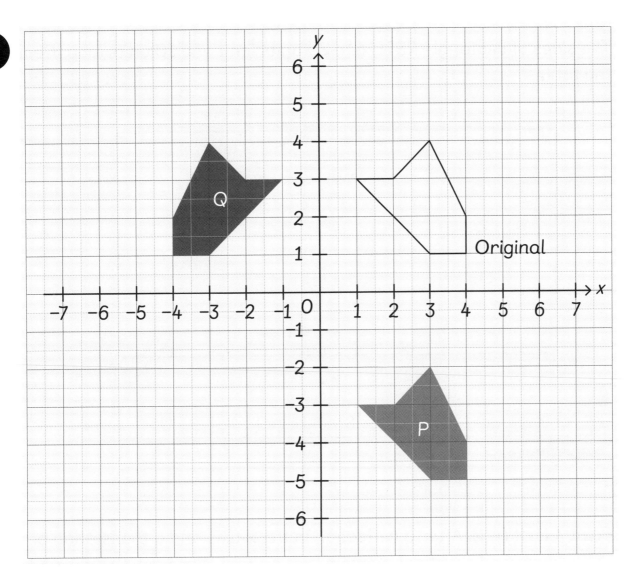

4

(a) Describe the movement that gets the shape from the original position to that of P.

(b) Describe the movement that gets the shape from the original position to that of Q.

5 The sides of rectangle RSTU are 20 units long and 10 units long. Complete the table.

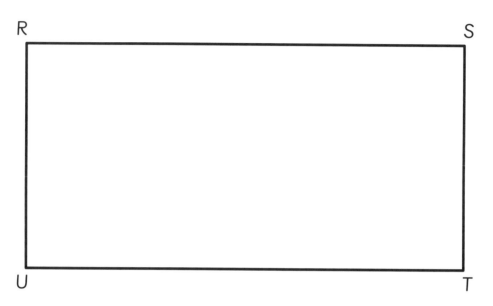

point	R	S	T	U
coordinates	(a, b)			

6 Point X is at (x, y). After a reflection in the x-axis and a translation of 3 units downwards, its final position is at point Y. What are the coordinates of point Y?

The coordinates of point Y are (⬜ , ⬜).

Graphs and Averages

Chapter 14

Name: _____ Class: _____ Date: _____

Worksheet 1

Understanding Averages

There are 4 plates of biscuits.

On average, how many biscuits are there on each plate?

Suppose the number of biscuits on each plate is the same. On average, there would then be 6 biscuits on each plate.

Use ' method for the following questions.

1 The number of stars awarded to each group is shown below.

Group A	★ ★ ★ ★ ★ ★ ★ ★
Group B	★ ★ ★ ★
Group C	★ ★ ★ ★ ★ ★

On average, how many stars does each group receive?

2 The bar graph shows the number of pupils on each team.

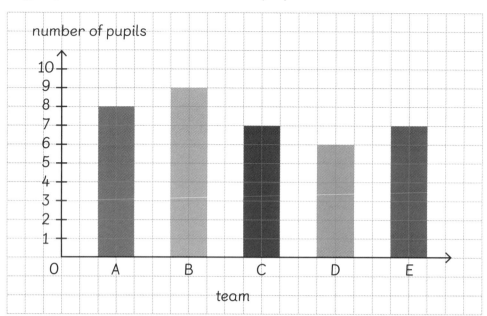

On average, how many pupils are on each team?

3 The graph shows the number of books some children read over four weeks.

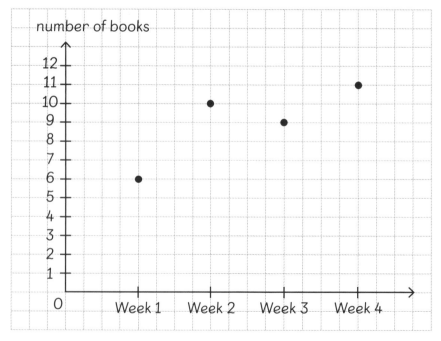

On average, how many books did the children read per week?

Worksheet 2

Calculating the Mean

1 This table shows the number of cars sold by some salespeople over 4 weeks.

Parker	4
Sophie	8
Emily	6
Bradley	9

(a) Calculate the mean number of cars sold by each salesperson per week.

(b) Calculate the mean number of cars sold by all the salespeople per week.

2 Emma's scores for 5 different quizzes are shown below.

Quiz 1 ⑧
Quiz 2 ⑦
Quiz 3 ⑨
Quiz 4 ⑦
Quiz 5 ⑩ Excellent!

What is Emma's mean score?

3 Some pupils took 3 different quizzes and the score sheet below shows their scores.

	Hannah	Ravi	Lulu	Elliott
Quiz 1	8	6	7	9
Quiz 2	8	7	9	10
Quiz 3	5	8	10	8

Two pupils have the same mean score. Which two pupils are these and what is their mean score?

Worksheet 3

Calculating the Mean

1 The members of three families and their ages are shown below.

The Smiths

42 years old

35 years old

10 years old

7 years old

The Joneses

64 years old

32 years old

28 years old

3 years old

2 years old

The Taylors

34 years old

29 years old

6 years old

1 year old

1 year old

1 year old

Calculate the mean age of each family. Which family has the highest mean age?

2 Amira buys 3 oranges that have a total mass of 450 g.

(a) Find the mean mass per orange.

[   ]

(b) Is it possible that all 3 oranges have the same mass? Explain your answer.

[   ]

(c) Is it possible that all 3 oranges have different masses? Explain your answer.

[   ]

(d) Amira buys another 2 oranges and the mean mass of the oranges she has increases. Is it possible that all 5 oranges have the same mass? Explain your answer.

[   ]

Worksheet 4

Solving Problems Involving the Mean

1 4 boys have a mean height of 162 cm. Another boy with a height of 165 cm joins them. What is the new mean height?

2 The mean age of a family with two adults and two children is 21.5 years old. Given that the mean age of the two adults is 29.5 years old, what is the mean age of the two children?

3 This table shows Holly's marks for five consecutive tests.

	test 1	test 2	test 3	test 4	test 5
score	98	?	79	85	?

(a) Her mean score for the five tests is 90.4. Find the mean score for test 2 and test 5.

(b) For each test, the maximum score is 100. Find the highest and the lowest possible value for Holly's score in test 5.

Highest:

Lowest:

Worksheet 5

Showing Information on Graphs

1 This table shows the favourite colours of a group of 36 children.

blue	red	green	yellow	others
9	15	3	3	6

Show the information in a pie chart.

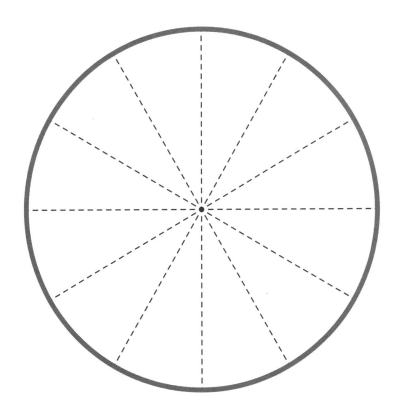

2 120 cookies of four different flavours are for sale at a bakery.

chocolate chip	50
vanilla	40
oatmeal	10
strawberry	20

Show the information in a pie chart.

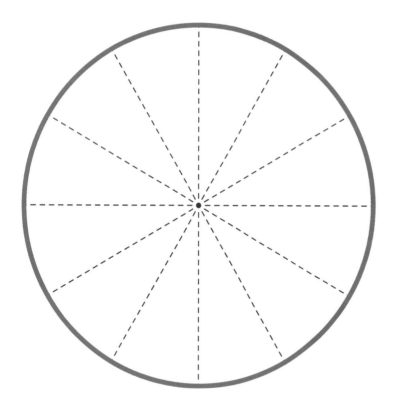

Name: _____ Class: _____ Date: _____

Worksheet 6

Reading Pie Charts

1 This pie chart shows the number of computers owned by 50 households in a town.

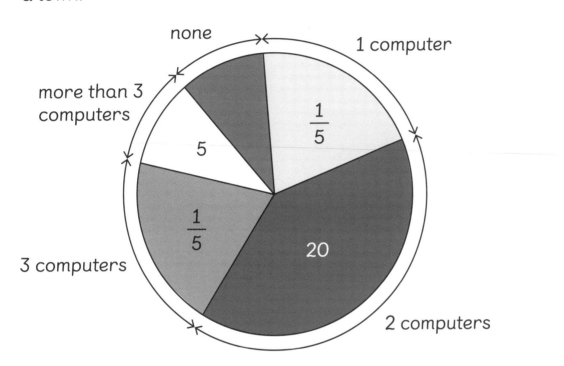

Complete the table.

number of computers	number of households
none	
one	
two	
three	
more than three	

2 The following pie chart and table show the number of vehicles of different types at a car park.

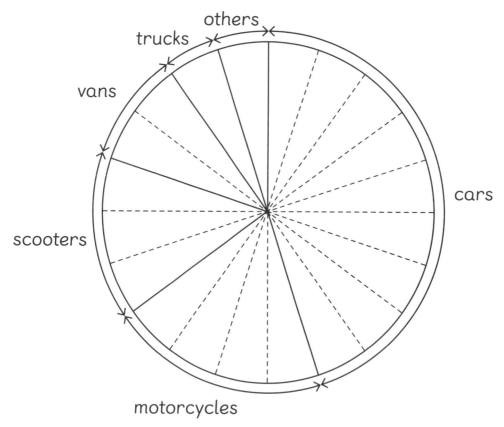

type of vehicles	number of vehicles
cars	a
motorcycles	$4b$
scooters	54
vans	$2c$
trucks	c
others	b

Find the values of a, b and c.

Name: _____ Class: _____ Date: _____

Worksheet 7

Reading Pie Charts

1 This pie chart shows the percentage of different kinds of books in a library.

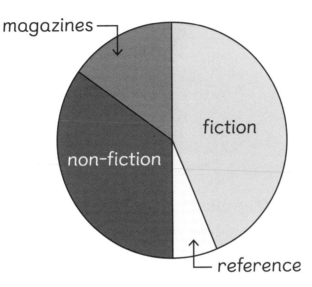

magazines

fiction

non-fiction

reference

Types of Books in a Library

(a) What percentage are fiction books?

(b) Are there more fiction or non-fiction books? What is the difference in percentage?

2 This pie chart from an athletics meeting shows the percentage of schools winning different numbers of medals.

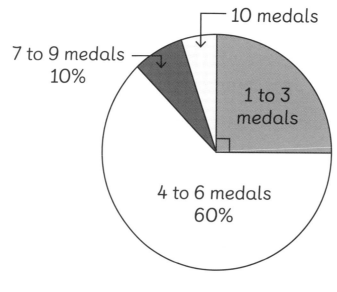

Medals Won by Schools

(a) How many schools won 0 medals? How many schools won 11 medals?

(b) Find the percentage of schools that won fewer than 4 medals.

(c) Given that 12 schools won 4 to 6 medals, how many schools won 10 medals?

Worksheet 8

Reading Pie Charts

1 This pie chart shows the percentages for different kinds of birds a bird watcher saw during one month.

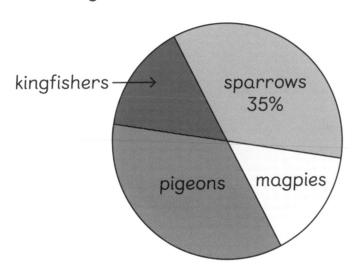

Birds Observed

The bird watcher saw 40 birds altogether. Find the number of each type of bird that he saw.

Magpie: [____]

Sparrow: [____]

Kingfisher: [____]

Pigeon: [____]

2 This pie chart shows the visitors to a zoo during a weekend.

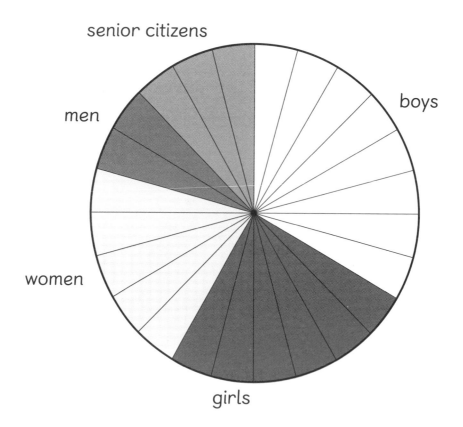

4800 people visited the zoo that weekend. Complete the table.

	number of people
boys	
girls	
women	
men	
senior citizens	

Name: _____ Class: _____ Date: _____

Worksheet 9

Reading Line Graphs

1 This graph shows the distance a bus travelled over one hour.

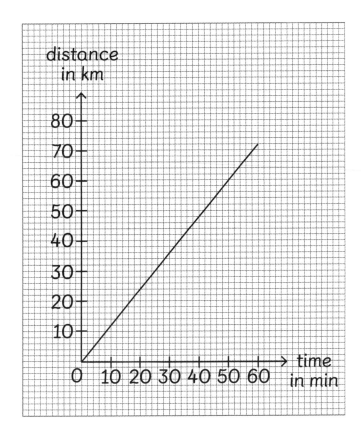

(a) How far did the bus travel in the first 10 minutes?

(b) How far did the bus travel in the first 30 minutes?

(c) How far did the bus travel in one hour?

(d) The speed of the bus (increased / decreased / remained unchanged) during the journey.

2 This graph shows the distance Sam ran during three hours.

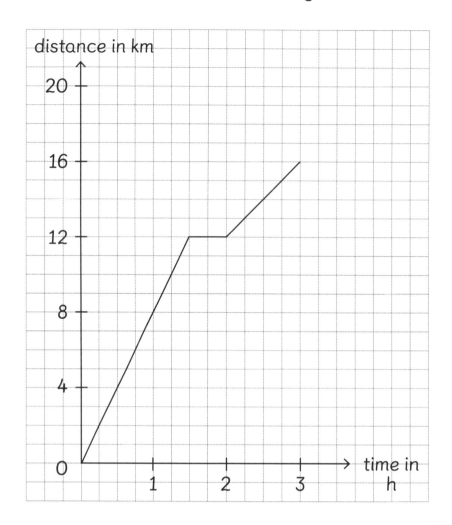

(a)   Find the distance Sam ran in the first hour.

(b)   Find the distance Sam ran over 3 hours.

(c)   (i)   Find the distance Sam ran before he stopped for a rest.

(ii)   For how long did he rest?

(d)   Did Sam run faster or slower after the rest?

Worksheet 10

Reading Line Graphs

1 This graph shows the number of toy cars a machine produces during a period of 10 minutes.

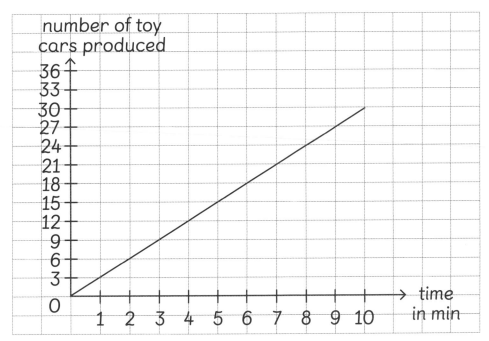

(a) How many toy cars does the machine produce in 1 minute?

(b) How many toy cars does the machine produce in 5 minutes?

(c) How long does the machine take to produce 21 toy cars?

(d) How long will the machine take to produce 36 toy cars?

2 This graph shows the wages a retail shop pays its employees on weekdays and at weekends.

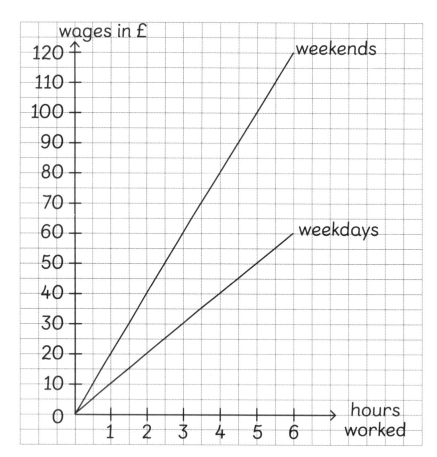

(a)   How much does an employee get for working 4 hours on a weekday?

(b)   How much does an employee get for working 9 hours at a weekend?

(c)   An employee works 4 hours on Friday, 5 hours on Saturday and
       3 hours on Sunday. How much is he paid?

(d)   An employee works 8 hours on both Wednesday and Saturday.
       How much more does she receive on Saturday than on Wednesday?

Worksheet 11

Converting Miles into Kilometres

1 Fill in the blanks.

(a)   0.5 miles   ≈ | 0.8 | km

(b)   0.75 miles   ≈ | 1.2 | km

(c)   1.2 miles   ≈ | 1.92 | km

(d)   2.25 miles   ≈ | 3.6 | km

(e)   0.4 km   ≈ | 0.25 | miles

(f)   1 km   ≈ | 0.625 | miles

(g)   24 km   ≈ | 15 | miles

(h)   560 km   ≈ | 350 | miles

3.2

0.125
5) 0.625

2 Here is a map of a neighbourhood.

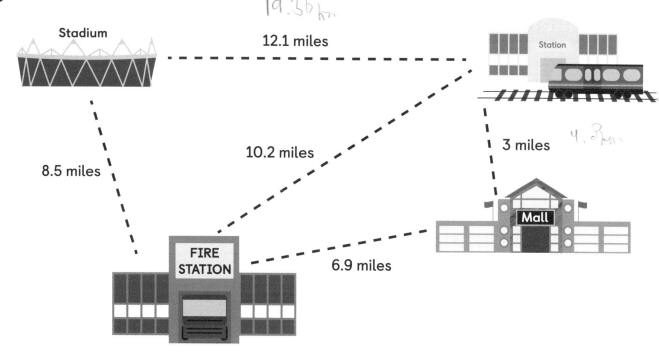

For each of the following questions, circle the distance that is the best estimate.

(a) The distance between the shopping mall and the train station is about:

(5 km)	8 km	10 km	12 km

(b) The distance between the stadium and the train station is about:

10 km	15 km	**(20 km)**	25 km

(c) The distance between the fire station and the shopping mall is about:

5 km	10 km	15 km	20 km

(d) The distance between the fire station and the stadium is about:

6 km	8 km	10 km	14 km

Worksheet 12

Reading Line Graphs

This graph shows how the US dollar is related to the Euro and to the Australian dollar.

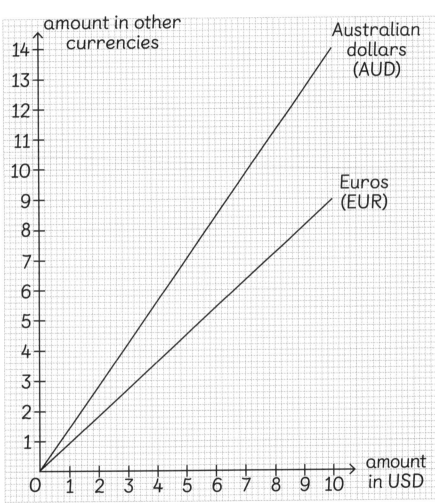

(a) A cup of coffee costs EUR €3.20. How much does it cost in USD?

(b) A tourist is going for a holiday in Australia. He wants to change $1000 USD to AUD. How much money should he get?

Date:_____

Ravi puts five number cards facing down.

He provides the following information:

• The average of the five numbers is 101.
• The average of the first three numbers counting from the right is 84.
• The average of the first three numbers counting from the left is 124.

What number is on the card in the centre?

Name: _____ Class: _____ Date: _____

Review 14

1 This table shows the number of points scored by teams in 3 quizzes.

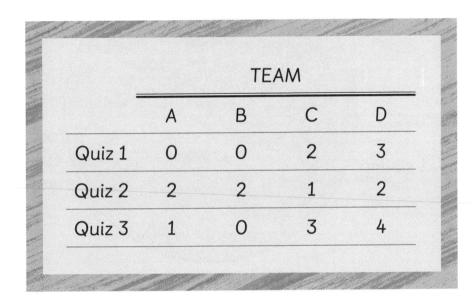

	TEAM			
	A	B	C	D
Quiz 1	0	0	2	3
Quiz 2	2	2	1	2
Quiz 3	1	0	3	4

(a) Find the mean number of points scored by each team.

Team A: [ ]

Team B: [ ]

Team C: [ ]

Team D: [ ]

(b) Find the mean number of the total number of points scored by all teams in each quiz.

[ ]

2 This pie chart shows the number of siblings some pupils have.

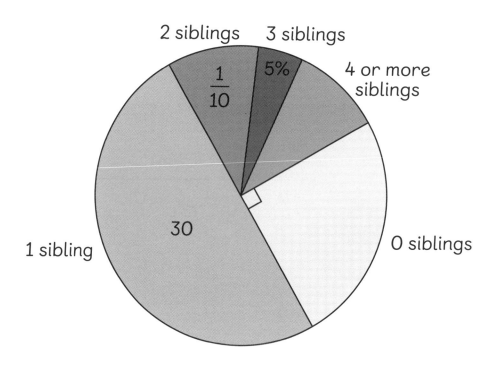

(a)   How many pupils do not have any siblings?

(b)   How many pupils have two siblings?

(c)   How many pupils have three siblings?

(d)   How many pupils have more than three siblings?

3 This graph shows the distance a motorcyclist travelled over 30 minutes.

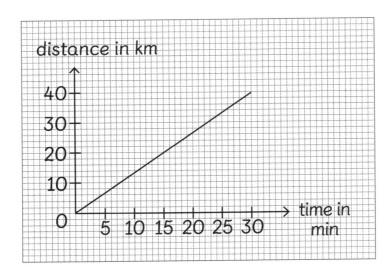

(a) Find the distance he travelled in the first 10 minutes.

(b) How long did he take to travel 40 km?

(c) If he does not stop for a rest, how far would he travel in one hour?

(d) Did the speed of the motorcycle increase, decrease or remain unchanged during the journey?

4 This graph shows how the data used affects the cost of two different pay-per-use mobile data plans.

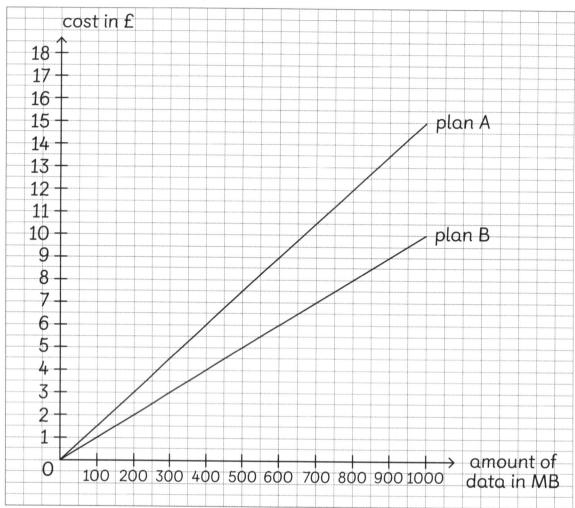

(a) Emma subscribes to plan A and uses 300 MB of data in one month. How much does she have to pay?

(b) Elliott subscribes to plan A and uses about 800 MB of data every month. How much will he save each month if he switches to plan B?

(c) In one month, Lulu and Hannah used the same amount of data. Given that Lulu paid £3.50 more than Hannah, how much data did each of them use?

Negative Numbers

Chapter 15

Name: _____ Class: _____ Date: _____

Worksheet 1

Adding and Subtracting Negative Numbers

1 Calculate the value of each of the following:

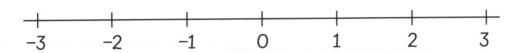

(a) $2 - 3 =$ [ ]

(b) $2 - 4 =$ [ ]

(c) $3 - 5 =$ [ ]

(d) $1 - 4 =$ [ ]

(e) $-3 + 4 =$ [ ]

(f) $-1 - 2 =$ [ ]

2 Find the value of:

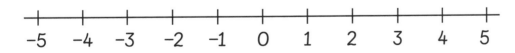

(a) $5 - 6 =$ [ ]

(b) $3 - 7 =$ [ ]

(c) $-2 - 3 =$ [ ]

(d) $-4 + 9 =$ [ ]

(e) $-5 + 7 =$ [ ]

(f) $0 - 3 =$ [ ]

3 Find the value of the following:

(a) −2 + 9 = [　　　]

(b) 7 − 9 = [　　　]

(c) −4 + 5 = [　　　]

(d) −1 − 7 = [　　　]

(e) 0 − 6 = [　　　]

(f) 4 − 10 = [　　　]

(g) 1 − 8 = [　　　]

(h) −6 + 6 = [　　　]

(i) −6 + 16 = [　　　]

(j) −12 − 8 = [　　　]

4

Given that  and ☾ represent 1-digit positive numbers, what could ♥ and ☾ be?

♥ [　　　]

☾ [　　　]

5 ♣ + ♠ = −8

Given that ♣ is a negative 1-digit number and ♠ is a positive whole number, what could ♣ and ♠ be?

♣ [　　　]

♠ [　　　]

Worksheet 2

Using Negative Numbers

1 In a 5-question Science quiz, 4 marks are awarded for each correct answer and 2 marks are deducted for each incorrect answer. No mark is awarded or deducted for questions which are not attempted. , , and took the quiz and the results are shown in this table.

	Number of correct answers	Number of incorrect answers	Not attempted
Ruby	2	2	1
Charles	1	3	1
Lulu	4	1	0
Ravi	2	3	0
Emma	1	4	0

Calculate the score of each student.

(a) Ruby

(b) Charles

(c) Lulu

(d) Ravi

(e) Emma

2 According to a website, the average temperature in the UK is about 5 °C in the month of January. Find the average temperature of each of the following cities.

(a) The average temperature in Bangkok, Thailand is 19 °C higher than in the UK.

(b) The average temperature in Seoul, Korea is 7 °C lower than in the UK.

(c) The average temperature in Beijing, China is 9 °C lower than in the UK.

Mind Workout ▶

Mr Smith's office is in a 50-storey building. One morning, he went up 6 floors for a meeting. After the meeting he went down 12 floors to the cafeteria for lunch. Then he went up 20 floors to the top floor to meet his manager. On which floor is Mr Smith's office located?

Review 15

1 Find the value.

(a) $6 - 9$ = [ ]

(b) $-6 + 9$ = [ ]

(c) $-6 - 9$ = [ ]

(d) $-9 + 6$ = [ ]

(e) $-8 - 3$ = [ ]

(f) $3 - 7$ = [ ]

(g) $-7 - 2$ = [ ]

(h) $0 - 4$ = [ ]

(i) $-3 + 3$ = [ ]

(j) $-5 - 7$ = [ ]

2 ⬤ + ⭐ = -4

⬤ represents a 1-digit positive whole number and ⭐ represents a 1-digit negative whole number. Write down 5 possible pairs of values represented by ⬤ and ⭐.

⬤	⭐

3 According to a website, the temperature in Beijing, China on 22 January 2016 was −6 °C. The next day, on 23 January, the temperature dropped by 7 °C. Then on 24 January, it rose 9 °C from the day before. Find the temperature:

(a)   on 23 January 2016

(b)   on 24 January 2016

4 Fill in the blanks.

(a)

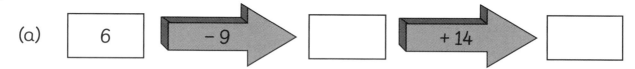

| 6 | → − 9 → | | → + 14 → | |

(b)

| −11 | → + 3 → | | → + 16 → | |

Revision 4

1

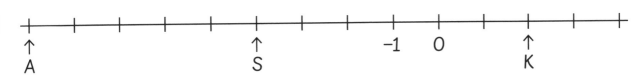

(a) What are the numbers represented by A, S and K?

(i) A ☐

(ii) S ☐

(iii) K ☐

(b) Find the difference between:

(i) the value of A and S ☐

(ii) the value of S and K ☐

(c) Mark and label these numbers on the number line:

(i) −6

(ii) 4

2 Find the volume of each cuboid.

(a)

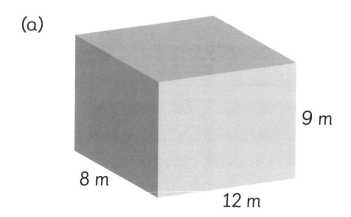

9 m

8 m

12 m

(b)

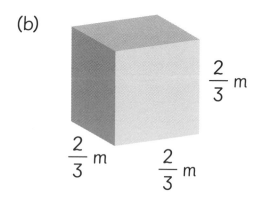

$\frac{2}{3}$ m

$\frac{2}{3}$ m

$\frac{2}{3}$ m

(c)

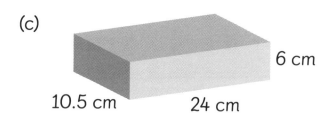

6 cm

10.5 cm

24 cm

(d)

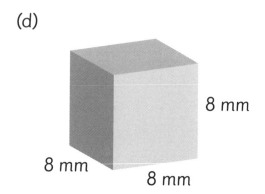

8 mm

8 mm

8 mm

3 What is the greatest possible number of 3-cm cubes that can fit inside this cuboid?

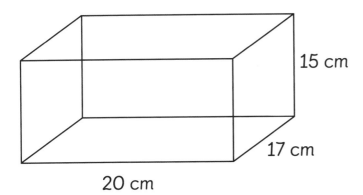

15 cm

17 cm

20 cm

4 Evaluate.

(a) −12 + 3 = ☐

(b) −5 − 7 = ☐

(c) 7 − 11 = ☐

(d) 3 − 16 = ☐

(e) 0 − 4 = ☐

(f) −7 + 17 = ☐

5 In this figure, VWX and XYZ are triangles. WXY and VXZ are straight lines. Find ∠XYZ.

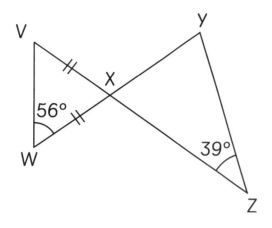

6 OB and OC are radii (or radiuses) of the circle. Given that ABCD is a rectangle, find ∠y.

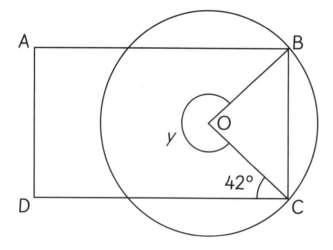

7

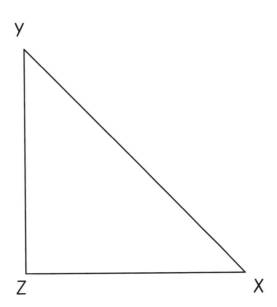

(a) Find the length.

   (i)   YZ

   (ii) XZ

   (iii) XY

(b) Measure.

   (i)   ∠YZX

   (ii) ∠YXZ

(c) Find the perimeter of triangle XYZ.

(d)   Draw another triangle ABC so that the ratio of the corresponding
       lengths in triangle XYZ and triangle ABC is always 2 : 1.

8 Point P starts out at (x, y). It is first reflected in the y-axis. The image is
then translated 10 units upwards and 5 units to the left to its final position
at Q. Find the coordinates of Q.

The coordinates of Q are (⬚ , ⬚).

9 The pie chart represents the different kinds of balls stored in a school equipment room. Altogether there are 120 balls in the equipment room. 50% of the balls are footballs and the ratio of the number of volleyballs to the number of rugby balls is 2 : 3.

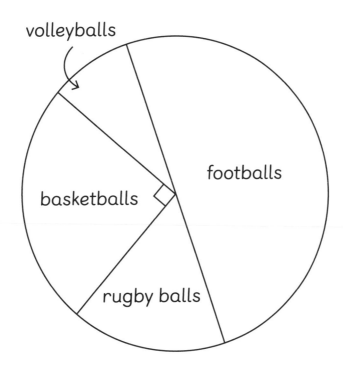

(a)   Find the number:

    (i)   of basketballs ☐

    (ii)   of rugby balls ☐

(b)   What percentage of the balls are volleyballs?

☐

(c)   Find the average number of each type of ball.

☐

10 This line graph shows the distance Elliott cycled during two hours.

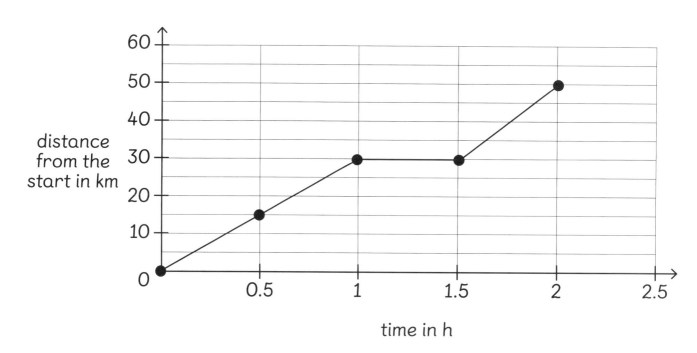

distance from the start in km

time in h

(a) How far did Elliott cycle in the first half hour?

(b) How far did Elliott cycle in the second hour?

(c) How far did Elliott cycle before he stopped for a rest and how long was his rest?

(d) Did Elliott increase or decrease his speed after the rest?

(e) Using 50 miles = 80 km, find the total distance Elliott cycled in miles.

End-of-Year Revision

Section A

Choose the correct answer.
Write the correct answer – (1), (2), (3) or (4) – in the brackets to the right.

1 $2\,036\,089 = 2\,000\,000 + 6000 + \boxed{\ ?\ } + 9$

   (1)   80
   (2)   3000
   (3)   3080
   (4)   30 080

   (   )

2 In the number 645.279, what is the value of the digit 7?

   (1)   7 tens
   (2)   7 tenths
   (3)   7 hundredths
   (4)   7 thousandths

   (   )

3 Find the value of $300 \div 10 - (4 + 5) \times 3$.

   (1)   2973
   (2)   273
   (3)   73
   (4)   3

   (   )

4 Which is the smallest fraction?

(1) $\dfrac{2}{3}$

(2) $\dfrac{4}{9}$

(3) $\dfrac{1}{2}$

(4) $\dfrac{3}{5}$

( )

5 Find the value of $98 \div 1000$.

(1) 0.098

(2) 0.98

(3) 9.8

(4) 98 000

( )

6 Find the value of $-4 - 9$.

(1) −5

(2) 5

(3) −13

(4) 13

( )

7 Which of the following is equal to 2 kg 30 g?

(1) 2.3 kg

(2) 2.03 kg

(3) 2300 g

(4) 230 g

( )

8 What are the coordinates of point M?

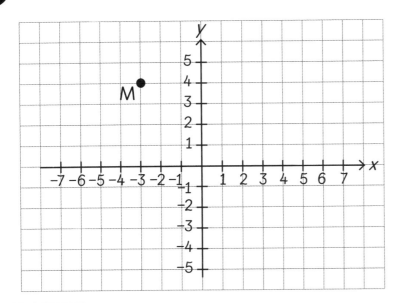

(1)   (4, -3)

(2)   (4, 3)

(3)   (-3, 4)

(4)   (-3, -4)

             (   )

9 Which of the following distances is the furthest?

(1)   12 000 cm

(2)   1 km

(3)   0.7 mile

(4)   999 m

             (   )

10 What is 75% of 320?

(1)   80

(2)   240

(3)   2400

(4)   24 000

             (   )

Section B

Write your answers in the spaces provided.

11 A whole number rounded to the nearest 100 000 is 4 000 000. What is the smallest possible value of the whole number?

12 Form the smallest possible 7-digit even number using all these digits.

| 5 | 7 | 0 | 8 | 3 | 9 | 1 |

13 Multiply.

$0.64 \times 7 =$?

14 Evaluate $\frac{1}{3}(2k + 10)$ when $k = 7$.

15 £1000 is shared among 40 people. How much will each person get?

16 List all the prime numbers between 50 and 70.

17 How much does each apple cost?

£1.38

18 12 : 16 = 9 : [?]

Find the missing number.

19 Add and show your answer as a mixed number in its simplest form.

$$\frac{2}{3} + \frac{2}{5} + \frac{2}{15}$$

20 Find the area of the outlined triangle.

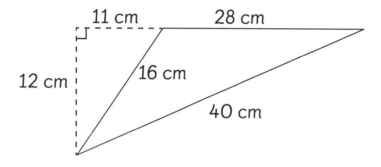

11 cm   28 cm

12 cm   16 cm

40 cm

21 30% of the pupils in a class wear glasses. There are 20 pupils in the class. How many pupils in the class do not wear glasses?

22 List all the common factors of 18 and 30.

23 Multiply and give your answer in the simplest form.

$$\frac{2}{3} \times \frac{9}{16}$$

24 Find the volume of the cuboid.

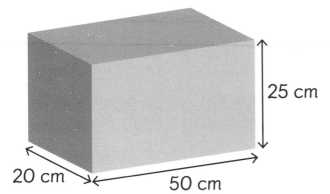

25 cm

20 cm   50 cm

25 What is 6.9 more than Y?

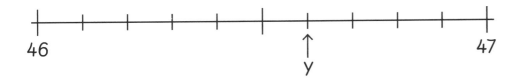

46   47

Y

26 3 h 24 min = $\boxed{\quad ? \quad}$ h

Find the missing number.

$\boxed{}$

27 The sum of 6 numbers is 102. What is the mean of the 6 numbers?

$\boxed{}$

28 1.4 l of syrup is poured equally into 23 small bottles with 20 ml left over. What is the capacity of each bottle?

$\boxed{}$

29 Given that the perimeter of the rectangle is 36 cm, find the length of its longer side.

7 cm

$\boxed{}$

30 $\frac{3}{4}$ of a cake was shared equally among 4 people. What fraction of the

cake did each of them get?

```

```

31 The price shown is after a 40% discount. Calculate the original price of
the pair of shoes.

Reduced
£84

```

```

32 The ratio of the value of $\angle y$ to that of $\angle z$ is 7 : 8. Find $\angle z$.

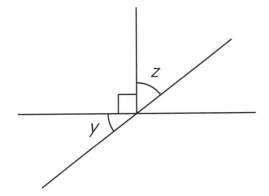

```

```

33 O is the centre of the circle and NOR is the diameter. Given that MNOP is a square, find ∠QOR.

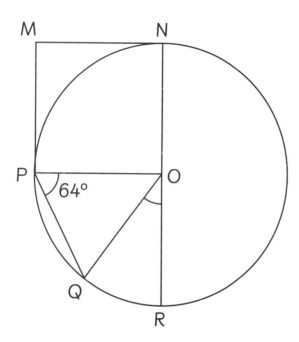

34 What is the greatest possible number of 4-cm cubes that can be packed into a 50-cm cube?

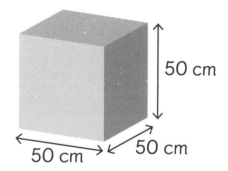

50 cm

50 cm

50 cm

35 Calculate the mean of all the odd numbers between 20 and 30.

36 The line graph shows how to calculate the wages of the chefs in a restaurant based on the number of hours they work.

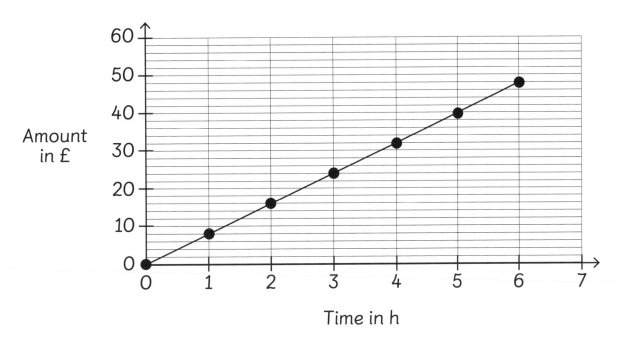

Time in h

(a) A chef worked for 5 hours. How much was he paid?

(b) A chef was paid £32. How many hours did he work?

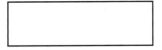

(c) The chefs are paid twice as much for working on public holidays. Chef Green worked 6 hours last Christmas. How much was he paid that day?

37 People in a survey were asked to choose their favourite colour. This table shows the result of the survey.

Colour	Black	White	Blue	Green
Number of people	180	120	224	?

(a) More people chose black than white. How many more chose black as a percentage?

(b) What is the ratio of the number of people who chose blue to the number of people who chose white? Show your answer in the simplest form.

(c) 20% fewer people chose green than chose black as their favourite colour. How many people chose green as their favourite colour?

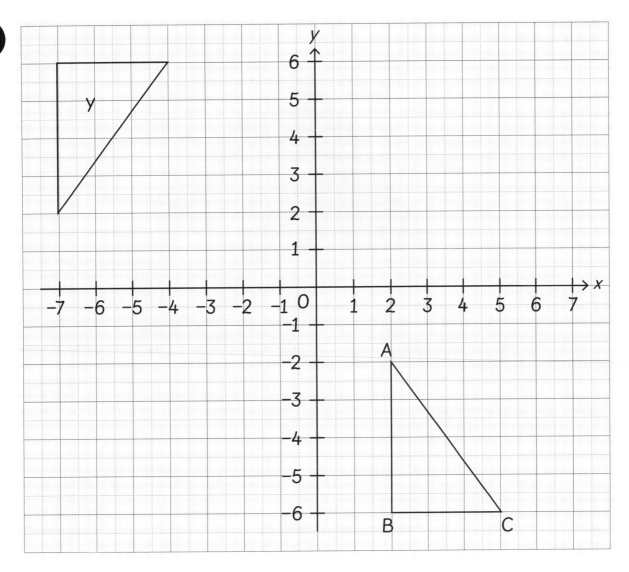

(a) Draw to show ABC when it is reflected in the *x*-axis and in the *y*-axis.

(b) Describe the movement that moves triangle ABC from its original position to Y.

39 Draw a net for this figure.

40 The ratio of the sides of a triangle are 3 : 4 : 7. The perimeter of the triangle is 84 cm. Find the length of the shortest side of the triangle.

Section C

Solve the word problems.

Show your work clearly.

41 40% of the paper clips in a box are blue, 50% of those remaining are red and the rest are green. There are 153 green paper clips. How many paper clips are there in the box?

42 The mean weight of four girls and two boys is 42.5 kg. The mean weight of the four girls is 38.5 kg. Find the mean weight of the two boys.

43 This year, the ratio of Charles' age to his father's age is 2 : 7. The ratio of his father's age to his grandfather's age is 1 : 2. Charles' grandfather is 70 years old.

(a) How old is Charles' father?

(b) How old will Charles be in 5 years' time?

44 arranged some black and white square tiles according to a rule.

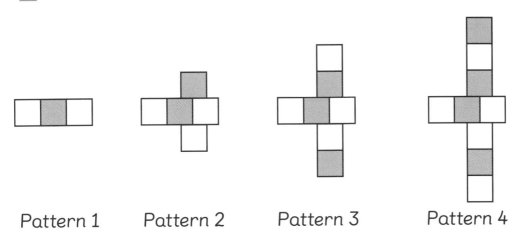

Pattern 1   Pattern 2   Pattern 3   Pattern 4

(a) Complete the table.

Pattern number, n	Number of white squares	Number of black squares	Total number of squares
1	2	1	3
2	3	2	5
3	4	3	7
4	5	4	9
6			

(b) Write an algebraic expression in terms of n to find the total number of squares in Pattern n.

45 A 6.4-m long rope is cut into three parts of different lengths. The ratio of the length of the first part to the length of the second part is 4 : 5. The last part is 80 cm longer than the second part. Find the length of the longest part in metres.